# Groundworks®

## Reasoning with Numbers

# 6

Carole Greenes • Carol Findell
Barbara Irvin • Rika Spungin

 Wright Group

# Acknowledgments

**Dr. Carole Greenes**
is a professor of
Mathematics Education
at Boston University.
She has written and
collaborated on more
than 200 publications,
and her work has
brought teachers and
students closer to
the NCTM Standards.
Dr. Greenes was
recently inducted into
the Massachusetts
Mathematics Educators
Hall of Fame.

**Dr. Carol Findell**
is a Clinical Associate
Professor of Education
at Boston University.
She has served as a
mathematics educator
for more than 30 years,
during which time she
has led writing teams for
national mathematics
competitions. Dr. Findell
is a well-respected
author and is a frequent
speaker at national
mathematics conferences.

**Dr. Rika Spungin**
is a Professor Emeritus
of Mathematics Education.
She has co-authored
many publications that
develop problem-solving
skills in all learners.
Dr. Spungin's other goal
is that teachers enjoy
teaching mathematics.

**Dr. Barbara Irvin,**
is an educational
mathematics consultant.
She has authored
more than 30 activity
resource books. Dr. Irvin
is a former middle-school
teacher, mathematics
editor, and university
professor.

# www.WrightGroup.com

 **Wright Group**

Printed in the United States of America.

Send all inquiries to:
Wright Group/McGraw-Hill
P.O. Box 812960
Chicago, Illinois 60681

ISBN: 1-4045-2032-5

1 2 3 4 5 6 7 8 9 MAL 09 08 07 06 05 04

The **McGraw·Hill** Companies

# Contents

## Why Teach *Reasoning with Numbers* to Your Students?

In their 1989 *Curriculum and Evaluation Standards for School Mathematics* and again in their 2000 *Principles and Standards for School Mathematics*, the National Council of Teachers of Mathematics stressed the importance of not only learning to compute, but also of learning to reason with and about numbers. The Council recommended that curricula be designed to develop students' understanding of different ways in which numbers can be represented, of operations and how they are related to one another, of properties of operations on various sets of numbers, of number theory ideas, and of methods of computation and estimation. The Council also pointed out that students should be provided with opportunities to develop number sense.

Historically, elementary and middle-school mathematics have focused on arithmetic, the study of numbers, and operations with numbers. Students learned to count, compare, and order numbers, and to add, subtract, multiply, and divide with whole numbers, fractions, and decimals. Although these topics have been recommended for study for quite some time, most curricula deal primarily with the reading and writing of numbers and with computational algorithms. Few programs systematically, within and among grades, develop students' abilities to reason about and with numbers. *Groundworks: Reasoning with Numbers* introduces students to five big ideas of Number using interesting and challenging problems, and provides a sequence across grades that leads to greater understanding of number concepts and skills.

## Bibliography

Gay, A. Susan and Douglas B. Aichele, "Middle School Students' Understanding of Number Sense Related to Percent." *School Science and Mathematics* 97 (January 1997): 27–36.

Greenes, Carole, Linda Schulman, and Rika Spungin. *Thinkermath: Developing Number Sense & Arithmetic Skills, Grades 6–7.* Parsippany, Sunnyvale, CA: Creative Publications, 1989.

Harlos, Carol Ann. "And the Winner Is." *Mathematics Teaching in the Middle School 1,* (September–October 1995): 450–453.

Kilpatrick, Jeremy, Jane Swafford, and Bradford Findell (Eds.). *Adding It Up: Helping Children Learn Mathematics.* Washington, DC: National Academy Press, 2001.

Morrow, Lorna and Margaret Kenney (Eds.). *The Teaching and Learning of Algorithms in School Mathematics.* Reston, VA: National Council of Teachers of Mathematics, 1998.

National Council of Teachers of Mathematics. *Curriculum and Evaluation Standards for School Mathematics.* Reston, VA: The Council, 1989.

National Council of Teachers of Mathematics. *Principles and Standards for School Mathematics.* Reston, VA: The Council, 2000.

Reys, Barbara J. "Promoting Number Sense in the Middle Grades." *Mathematics Teaching in the Middle School 1,* (September–October 1994): 114–120.

## What Are the Five Big Ideas of *Reasoning with Numbers*?

*Groundworks: Reasoning with Numbers* for grades 1–7 provides challenging development of five big ideas of numbers. Problems build upon what students know about numbers and operations with numbers and broaden and solidify their conceptual understanding. The five big ideas are:

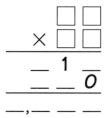

### Representation
Representation refers to the different ways in which numbers can be displayed. For example, 56 might be represented by its word name "fifty-six;" in expanded notation form as $50 + 6$ or $(5 \times 10 + 6 \times 1)$ or $(5 \times 10^1 + 6 \times 10^0)$; as the product of two numbers $(7 \times 8)$; or as a group of 56 objects. Students interpret and construct different representations of numbers.

The estimate of the sum of my three numbers is 5.

### Number Sense
Number sense involves making decisions about the types of numbers and the magnitudes of those numbers in order to solve problems in real-world contexts. Students round numbers in order to estimate quantities and amounts of money and the results of computations.

### Ratio and Proportion
A proportion is two equivalent ratios. A proportion shows how numbers vary in relation to one another. Students reason about proportions when they compute unit costs, generate equivalent fractions and ratios, compute with percentages, and identify parts of groups. Emphasis is placed on interpreting the language of proportionality (e.g., "For every one of these, there are four of those.").

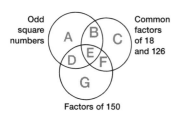

### Number Theory
Number theory is the study of the properties of the counting numbers. Students explore odd and even numbers, prime and composite numbers, multiples and factors of numbers, the least common multiples and the greatest common factors of sets of numbers, and rules of divisibility.

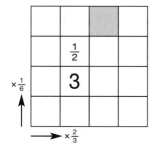

### Computation
Computation refers to operations with numbers. Operations include addition, subtraction, multiplication, and division with various types of numbers, including whole numbers, fractions, decimals, and integers. Students explore the algorithms and, as a consequence, gain greater understanding of the relationships between operations.

## What Is in this Book?

This book contains:

- 15 blackline-master problem sets (90 pages of problems)
- solutions for all problems
- specific teaching suggestions and ideas for each problem set
- general teacher information

## Problem Sets

Each problem set consists of eight pages. The first page presents teaching information, including goals listing specific mathematical reasoning processes or skills, questions to ask students, and solutions to the first problem. The next six pages are all reproducible problem pages. The first problem is a teaching problem and is of medium difficulty. The remaining five problems in the set range from easier to harder. Solutions to all problems are given on the eighth page of each problem set. For most problems, one solution method is shown; however, students may offer other valid methods. The mathematics required for the problems is in line with the generally approved mathematics curriculum for the grade level.

## How to Use this Book

Because many of the problem types will be new to your students, you may want to have the entire class or a large group of students work on the first problem in a set at the same time. You can use the questions that accompany the problem as the basis for a class discussion. As the students work on the problem, help them with difficulties they may encounter. Students are frequently asked to explain their thinking. You may choose to do this orally with the whole class. After students have several experiences telling about their thinking and hearing the thinking of others, they are usually better able to write about their own thinking. Once students have completed the first problem in a set, you may want to assign the remaining problems for students to do on their own or in pairs in class or for homework. If students have difficulty with the first problem in the set, you might do more of the problems with the whole class.

Although the big ideas and the families of problems within them come in a certain order, your students need not complete them in this order. Students might work the problem sets based on the mathematical content of the problems and their alignment with your curriculum or according to student interests or needs.

There is a Management Chart that you may duplicate for each student to keep in a portfolio. You may award the Certificate of Excellence upon the successful completion of the problem sets for each big idea.

# Management Chart

Name _____  Class _____  Teacher _____

| BIG IDEA | PROBLEM SET | | | | DATE |
|---|---|---|---|---|---|
| ★☆☆☆☆ **Representation** | Mystery Number | 1 | 2 | 3 | |
| | | 4 | 5 | 6 | |
| | Place It Right | 1 | 2 | 3 | |
| | | 4 | 5 | 6 | |
| ★★☆☆☆ **Number Sense** | Fit the Facts | 1 | 2 | 3 | |
| | | 4 | 5 | 6 | |
| | Fraction Distraction | 1 | 2 | 3 | |
| | | 4 | 5 | 6 | |
| ★★★☆☆ **Ratio and Proportion** | Best Buy | 1 | 2 | 3 | |
| | | 4 | 5 | 6 | |
| | Ratio Roundup | 1 | 2 | 3 | |
| | | 4 | 5 | 6 | |
| ★★★★☆ **Number Theory** | Number, Please! | 1 | 2 | 3 | |
| | | 4 | 5 | 6 | |
| | Which Region? | 1 | 2 | 3 | |
| | | 4 | 5 | 6 | |
| ★★★★★ **Computation** | Beanbag Toss | 1 | 2 | 3 | |
| | | 4 | 5 | 6 | |
| | Fraction Squares | 1 | 2 | 3 | |
| | | 4 | 5 | 6 | |
| | Grid Sums | 1 | 2 | 3 | |
| | | 4 | 5 | 6 | |
| | Globs of Goo | 1 | 2 | 3 | |
| | | 4 | 5 | 6 | |
| | Circle Sums | 1 | 2 | 3 | |
| | | 4 | 5 | 6 | |
| | Shape Numbers | 1 | 2 | 3 | |
| | | 4 | 5 | 6 | |
| | Order, Please! | 1 | 2 | 3 | |
| | | 4 | 5 | 6 | |

# Mystery Number

**Goals**
- Identify place values of digits in a decimal number from hundredths through thousands.
- Compute with decimal numbers.
- Use logical reasoning to solve problems.

**Notes**
Encourage students to draw six blanks to represent the digits. As students analyze the clues, they can list possible digits for each position and then cross out the ones that do not fit all of the clues.

Solutions to all problems in this set appear on page 7.

**Mystery Number 1**

**Questions to Ask**
- (Write the number 3,174.52 on the board.) What digit is in the tenths place? (5) The tens place? (7) How many digits are to the right of the decimal point? (2)
- Read Clue 1. How many thousands are in the mystery number? (3) How do you know? (All numbers from 3,000 to 3,200 have a 3 in the thousands place.)
- How many hundreds are in the mystery number? (0 or 1) How do you know? (All numbers from 3,001 through 3,199 have a 0 or a 1 in the hundreds place.)
- Read Clue 4. What is the digit in the ones place? (0) How do you know? (For the product of 5 and some number to equal 0, the digit in the ones place must be 0.)

**Solutions**
1. 3,140.75
2. Possible answer: From Clue 1, the thousands digit is 3 and the hundreds digit is 0 or 1. From Clue 4, the ones digit is 0. Because all of the digits are different (Clue 2), the hundreds digit is 1. From Clue 3, the digit in the hundredths place is 0 or 5. Because the ones digit is 0, the hundredths digit is 5. From Clue 5, the digit in the tenths place is 7. From Clue 6, the digit in the tens place is 7 − 3, or 4.

# Mystery Number  1

Use the clues to figure out the six-digit decimal number.

## Clues

**1** It is greater than 3,000 and less than 3,200.

**2** All of the digits are different.

**3** The digit in the hundredths place is a multiple of 5.

**4** The product of 5 and the digit in the ones place is 0.

**5** The digit in the tenths place is greater than 5 and is not a multiple of 3 or 4.

**6** The digit in the tens place is 3 less than the digit in the tenths place.

1. What is the mystery number? _____

2. How did you figure it out?

# Mystery Number ★ 2

Use the clues to figure out the five-digit decimal number.

## Clues

**1** It is between 200 and 210.

**2** All of the digits are different.

**3** The ones digit is half the tenths digit.

**4** The hundredths digit is 3 times the ones digit.

1. What is the mystery number? _____

2. How did you figure it out?

_____

_____

_____

_____

# Mystery Number ★ 3

Use the clues to figure out the six-digit decimal number.

**Clues**

**1**  It is between 7,000 and 7,200.

**2**  It is 0.05 less than a whole number.

**3**  All of the digits are odd numbers.

**4**  The digit in the tens place is the same as the digit in the tenths place.

**5**  The sum of the tens digit and the ones digit is 16.

1. What is the mystery number? _____

2. How did you figure it out?

_____

_____

_____

_____

# Mystery Number ★ 4

Use the clues to figure out the six-digit decimal number.

## Clues

**1** It is between 1,200 and 1,400.

**2** The tenths and hundredths digits are the same.

**3** The digit in the ones place is the only even number.

**4** The sum of the digit in the tenths place and the digit in the hundredths place is 10.

**5** The sum of the digit in the tens place and the digit in the ones place is 15.

**6** The digit in the tens place is not a multiple of 3.

1. What is the mystery number? _____

2. How did you figure it out?

_____

_____

_____

_____

# Mystery Number ★5★

Use the clues to figure out the six-digit decimal number.

**Clues**

**1** It is greater than 6,400 and less than 6,600.

**2** All of the digits are different.

**3** If 0.42 is added to the mystery number, the sum is a whole number.

**4** The difference between the tens digit and the hundreds digit is the same as the difference between the hundredths digit and the tenths digit.

**5** The digit in the hundreds place is an even number.

**6** The product of the ones digit and the hundredths digit is the hundredths digit.

1. What is the mystery number? _____

2. How did you figure it out?

_____

_____

_____

_____

# Mystery Number  6

Use the clues to figure out the six-digit decimal number.

**Clues**

**1** It is between 7,300 and 7,500.

**2** The hundreds digit is 2 less than the hundredths digit.

**3** The sum of the tens digit and the tenths digit is the thousands digit.

**4** The product of the hundreds digit and the ones digit is 32.

**5** The sum of the hundreds digit and the tens digit is the thousands digit.

1. What is the mystery number? _____

2. How did you figure it out?

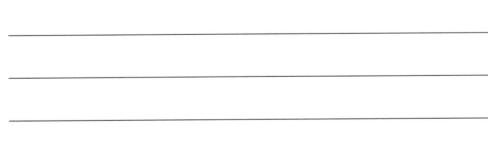

_____

_____

_____

_____

# Solutions

## Mystery Number  1

1. 3,140.75

2. Possible answer: From Clue 1, the thousands digit is 3 and the hundreds digit is 0 or 1. From Clue 4, the ones digit is 0. Because all of the digits are different (Clue 2), the hundreds digit is 1. From Clue 3, the digit in the hundredths place is 0 or 5. Because the ones digit is 0, the hundredths digit is 5. From Clue 5, the digit in the tenths place is 7. From Clue 6, the digit in the tens place is 7 − 3, or 4.

## Mystery Number  2

1. 203.69

2. Possible answer: From Clue 1, the hundreds digit is 2 and the tens digit is 0. From Clue 4, the hundredths digit is 9 and the ones digit is 3. From Clue 3, the tenths digit is 6, because 3 is half of 6.

## Mystery Number  3

1. 7,197.95

2. Possible answer: From Clue 1, the thousands digit is 7 and the hundreds digit is 0 or 1. From Clue 3, the digit in the hundreds place is 1. From Clue 2, the digit in the tenths place is 9 and the digit in the hundredths place is 5. From Clue 4, the digit in the tens place is 9. From Clue 5, the digit in the ones place is 7.

## Mystery Number  4

1. 1,378.55

2. Possible answer: From Clue 1, the thousands digit is 1 and the hundreds digit is 2 or 3. From Clue 3, only the ones digit is even, so the hundreds digit is 3. From Clues 2 and 4, the digit in the tenths place and hundredths place is 5. From Clues 3 and 5, the tens digit is 7 and the ones digit is 8, or the tens digit is 9 and the ones digit is 6. From Clue 6, the digit in the tens place is 7 and the digit in the ones place is 8.

## Mystery Number  5

1. 6,471.58

2. Possible answer: From Clue 1, the digit in the thousands place is 6 and the digit in the hundreds place is 4 or 5. From Clue 5, the digit in the hundreds place is 4. From Clue 3, the digit in the tenths place is 5, and the digit in the hundredths place is 8. From Clue 6, the ones digit is 1. From Clue 4, the digit in the tens place is 7.

## Mystery Number  6

1. 7,438.46

2. Possible answer: From Clue 1, the thousands digit is 7 and the hundreds digit is 3 or 4. From Clue 4, the hundreds digit is 4 and the ones digit is 8. From Clue 5, the tens digit is 3. From Clue 3, the tenths digit is 4. From Clue 2, the hundredths digit is 6.

# Place It Right

**Goals**
- Identify values of digits in whole numbers.
- Construct two- and three-digit numbers that, when multiplied, will have products that match given clues.

**Notes**
Encourage students to use estimation to establish the relationship between the tens digits of the two-digit factors. For example, in Problem 1, using 4 and 5 in the tens place of each factor gives a 2 in the thousands place of the product, which is too great.

**Solutions to all problems in this set appear on page 15.**

**Place It Right 1**

**Questions to Ask**
- Look at Problem 1. What number belongs in the thousands place in the product? (1) How do you know? (All numbers between 1,000 and 1,300 have a 1 in the thousands place.)
- Which digits are multiplied to get the 1 in the product? (The tens digits of both factors)
- Which pairs of numbers in the cloud could be the tens digits of the factors? (2 and 4, 2 and 5, or 2 and 7)
- How can you get a 5 in the ones place in the product? (Use the digits 5 and 7 in the ones place.)

**Solutions**

1.
```
    45
 ×  27
   315
   900
 1,215
```

2.
```
    72
 ×  45
   360
  2880
 3,240
```

# Place It Right ★ 1

Complete each multiplication. Use all of
the numbers in the cloud in each problem.

1. Put one number in each square so that
   • the product is between 1,000 and 1,300.
   • there is a 5 in the ones place in the product.

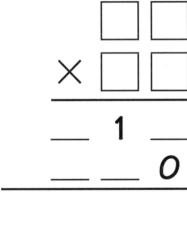

2. Put one number in each square so that
   • the product is between 3,000 and 3,300.
   • there is a 0 in the ones place in the product.

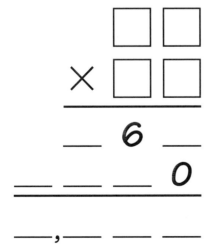

# Place It Right ★ 2

Complete each multiplication. Use all of
the numbers in the cloud in each problem.

1. Put one number in each square so that
   • the product is between 1,000 and 1,300.
   • there is a 4 in the ones place in the product.

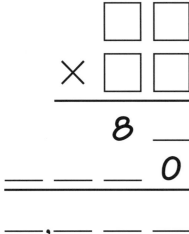

$$
\begin{array}{r}
\square\,\square \\
\times\ \square\,\square \\
\hline
8\ \underline{\phantom{0}} \\
\underline{\phantom{0}}\ \underline{\phantom{0}}\ \underline{\phantom{0}}\ 0 \\
\hline
\underline{\phantom{0}},\underline{\phantom{0}}\ \underline{\phantom{0}}\ \underline{\phantom{0}}
\end{array}
$$

2. Put one number in each square so that
   • the product is between 2,000 and 2,300.
   • there is a 2 in the ones place in the product.

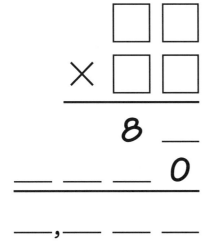

$$
\begin{array}{r}
\square\,\square \\
\times\ \square\,\square \\
\hline
8\ \underline{\phantom{0}} \\
\underline{\phantom{0}}\ \underline{\phantom{0}}\ \underline{\phantom{0}}\ 0 \\
\hline
\underline{\phantom{0}},\underline{\phantom{0}}\ \underline{\phantom{0}}\ \underline{\phantom{0}}
\end{array}
$$

# Place It Right ★ 3

Complete each multiplication. Use all of
the numbers in the cloud in each problem.

1. Put one number in each square so that
   • the product is between 2,000 and 2,300.
   • there is a 7 in the ones place in the product.

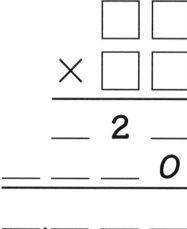

2. Put one number in each square so that
   • the product is between 4,000 and 4,500.
   • there is a 3 in the ones place in the product.

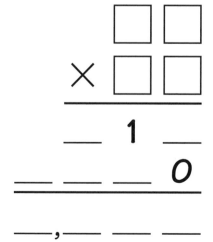

# Place It Right  4

Complete each multiplication. Use all of the numbers in the cloud in each problem.

1. Put one number in each square so that
   • the product is between 1,400 and 1,500.
   • there is a 0 in the ones place in the product.

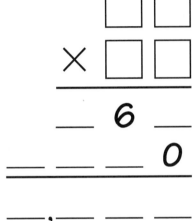

2. Put one number in each square so that
   • the product is between 2,000 and 2,300.
   • there is a 6 in the ones place in the product.

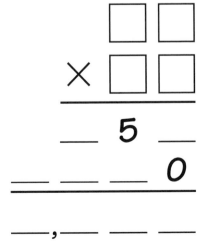

# Place It Right ⭐ 5

Complete each multiplication. Use all of
the numbers in the cloud in each problem.

1. Put one number in each square so that
   • the product is between 5,500 and 6,000.
   • there is a 0 in the ones place in the product.

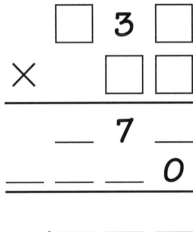

2. Put one number in each square so that
   • the product is between 7,000 and 7,500.
   • there is an 8 in the ones place in the product.

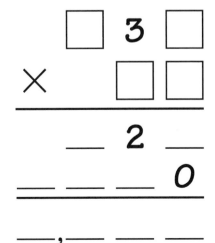

# Place It Right ⭐ 6

Complete each multiplication. Use all of
the numbers in the cloud in each problem.

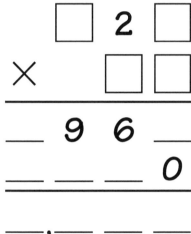

1. Put one number in each square so that
   • the product is between 5,000 and 5,300.
   • there is a 2 in the ones place in the product.

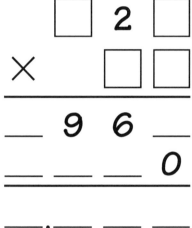

2. Put one number in each square so that
   • the product is between 8,000 and 8,500.
   • there is a 1 in the ones place in the product.

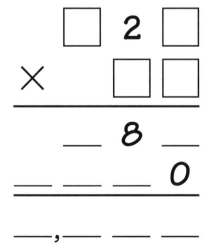

# Solutions

## Place It Right  1

1.　45
　× 27
　315
　900
1,215

2.　72
　× 45
　360
2880
3,240

## Place It Right  2

1.　21
　× 54
　84
1050
1,134

2.　41
　× 52
　82
2050
2,132

## Place It Right 3

1.　61
　× 37
　427
1830
2,257

2.　71
　× 63
　213
4260
4,473

## Place It Right  4

1.　32
　× 45
　160
1280
1,440

2.　52
　× 43
　156
2080
2,236

## Place It Right  5

1.　135
　× 42
　270
5400
5,670

2.　132
　× 54
　528
6600
7,128

## Place It Right  6

1.　327
　× 16
1962
3270
5,232

2.　127
　× 63
　381
7620
8,001

# Fit the Facts

**Goals**
- Compare magnitudes of whole numbers, decimals, and fractions.
- Compute with whole numbers, decimals, and fractions.
- Identify fractional parts of groups, including percents.
- Use proportional reasoning.

**Notes**
The order in which the blanks are filled in may vary. After completing the story, have students reread it to check that it makes number sense.

**Solutions to all problems in this set appear on page 23.**

### Fit the Facts 1

**Questions to Ask**
- Which blank in the story can you fill in first? (blank 1) How do you know? (The first day of summer is June 21.)
- Can you place 50 in the second blank? (No) Why not? (The total score for the two teams has to be the sum of two other numbers on the sign. No two numbers add to 50.)
- Where could you place 50 in the story? (In blank 3 as the percent)

**Solutions**
1. 21
2. 15
3. 50
4. 3
5. 9
6. 6

# Fit the Facts  1

Fill in the blanks with numbers from the sign.
Use each number once.
The story must make number sense.

On June _____ , the first day of summer, the Jets played
            (1)

the Stars in a baseball game. The two teams scored

a total of _____ runs. The Jets scored _____%,
            (2)                                  (3)

or _____ runs, more than the Stars. The Jets
      (4)

scored _____ runs. The Stars scored _____ runs.
           (5)                                (6)

# Fit the Facts  2

Fill in the blanks with numbers from the sign.
Use each number once.
The story must make number sense.

Mrs. Clark bought _____ bananas
(1)

and _____ peaches. She bought _____ % more
(2)                                      (3)

peaches than bananas. She bought _____ as many
(4)

apples as peaches, or _____ apples.
(5)

She bought _____ pieces of fruit in all.
(6)

# Fit the Facts ⭐ 3

Fill in the blanks with numbers from the sign.
Use each number once.
The story must make number sense.

75        5
    25
3          2
   1938

The original _____-cent coin was introduced in 1866.
                (1)

In the year _____, the coin was redesigned to look
              (2)

as it does today. The coin is _____% copper
                                  (3)

and _____% nickel. There is _____ times as much
       (4)                           (5)

copper as nickel in the coin. The diameter of the coin

is _____ centimeters.
     (6)

# Fit the Facts  4

Fill in the blanks with numbers from the sign.
Use each number once.
The story must make number sense.

In the bicycle store, there are _____ bicycles for
                                    (1)

every _____ tricycles. There are _____ more
          (2)                              (3)

bicycles than tricycles. Of the _____ cycles in the
                                    (4)

store, _____ are bicycles and _____ are tricycles.
           (5)                              (6)

# Fit the Facts ⭐ 5

Fill in the blanks with numbers from the sign.
Use each number once.
The story must make number sense.

The height of a person is about _____ times the length
(1)

of his or her head. Jack is 5 feet tall. The length of his head

is about _____ inches. The length of a person's head
(2)

is about $\frac{1}{3}$ of the length of that person's arm. Jack's arm is

about _____ feet long. The length of a person's head is
(3)

about _____ the length of that person's leg. Jack's leg
(4)

is about _____ inches, or _____ feet long.
(5)　　　　　　(6)

# Fit the Facts 6

Fill in the blanks with numbers from the sign.
Use each number once.
The story must make number sense.

66,600   253
240,000
365.25   93
1,110

In our solar system, Earth is about _____ million miles
                                          (1)

from the sun. It revolves around the sun at a speed

of about _____ miles per hour, or _____ miles
           (2)                              (3)

per minute. It takes Earth about _____ days to complete
                                      (4)

one revolution around the sun. Earth has one moon that

is about _____ miles away. The highest temperature
           (5)

on the moon's surface is about _____ degrees Fahrenheit,
                                    (6)

which is about 40 degrees more than the boiling point

of water on Earth.

# Solutions

### Fit the Facts ⭐ 1

1. 21
2. 15
3. 50
4. 3
5. 9
6. 6

### Fit the Facts ⭐ 2

1. 6
2. 12
3. 100
4. $\frac{1}{3}$
5. 4
6. 22

### Fit the Facts ⭐ 3

1. 5
2. 1938
3. 75
4. 25
5. 3
6. 2

### Fit the Facts ⭐ 4

1. 5
2. 2
3. 24
4. 56
5. 40
6. 16

### Fit the Facts ⭐ 5

1. 7.5
2. 8
3. 2
4. $\frac{1}{4}$
5. 32
6. $2\frac{2}{3}$

### Fit the Facts ⭐ 6

1. 93
2. 66,600
3. 1,100
4. 365.25
5. 240,000
6. 253

# Fraction Distraction

**Goals**
- Identify sets of mixed numbers whose totals match an estimated sum.
- Round fractions and mixed numbers.
- Add mixed numbers and fractions.

**Notes**
Prior to doing the problem set, review the rules for rounding with students. Point out that all fractions less than $\frac{1}{2}$ are rounded down and all fractions $\frac{1}{2}$ or greater are rounded up. Have students round all numbers on the sign to the nearest whole number before identifying the fractions or mixed numbers each person chose. Have students show all sums in simplest form.

**Solutions to all problems in this set appear on page 31.**

### Fraction Distraction 1

**Questions to Ask**
- What is $5\frac{1}{2}$ rounded to the nearest whole number? (6)
- What is $2\frac{1}{4}$ rounded to the nearest whole number? (2)
- Which mixed numbers on the sign, rounded to the nearest whole number, round to 1? ($1\frac{1}{4}$ and $\frac{3}{4}$)

**Solutions**
1. $3\frac{2}{3}$, $2\frac{1}{2}$, $\frac{1}{5}$ or $3\frac{2}{3}$, $2\frac{1}{2}$, $\frac{1}{3}$
2. $6\frac{11}{30}$ or $6\frac{1}{2}$
3. $1\frac{1}{4}$, $\frac{3}{4}$, $\frac{1}{5}$ or $1\frac{1}{4}$, $\frac{3}{4}$, $\frac{1}{3}$
4. $2\frac{1}{5}$ or $2\frac{1}{3}$

# Fraction Distraction  1

Alicia and Beth each chose three numbers from the sign and estimated their sum.

$3\frac{2}{3}$   $\frac{1}{5}$   $1\frac{1}{4}$   $2\frac{1}{2}$   $\frac{1}{3}$   $\frac{3}{4}$

The estimate of the sum of my three numbers is 7.

The estimate of the sum of my three numbers is 2.

**Alicia**          **Beth**

1. What are three numbers Alicia could have chosen?

   _____

2. What is the sum of those numbers?

   _____

3. What are three numbers Beth could have chosen?

   _____

4. What is the sum of those numbers?

   _____

# Fraction Distraction ★2

Carlos and Darryl each chose three numbers
from the sign and estimated their sum.

$\frac{1}{5}$   $\frac{3}{4}$

$1\frac{1}{2}$

$\frac{3}{5}$   $\frac{1}{3}$

$2\frac{1}{12}$

The estimate of the sum
of my three numbers is 1.

The estimate of the sum
of my three numbers is 5.

**Carlos**

**Darryl**

1. What are three numbers Carlos could have chosen?

   _____

2. What is the sum of those numbers?

   _____

3. What are three numbers Darryl could have chosen?

   _____

4. What is the sum of those numbers?

   _____

# Fraction Distraction  3

Kim and Fern each chose three numbers
from the sign and estimated their sum.

$1\frac{1}{3}$      $\frac{5}{8}$

$2\frac{1}{8}$

$1\frac{3}{4}$      $\frac{1}{4}$

$\frac{1}{2}$

The estimate of the sum
of my three numbers is 5.

The estimate of the sum
of my three numbers is 2.

**Kim**          **Fern**

1.  What are three numbers Kim could have chosen?

    _____

2.  What is the sum of those numbers?

    _____

3.  What are three numbers Fern could have chosen?

    _____

4.  What is the sum of those numbers?

    _____

# Fraction Distraction  4

Glen and Huang each chose three numbers
from the sign and estimated their sum.

$\frac{4}{5}$  $2\frac{1}{2}$

$2\frac{1}{15}$

$\frac{1}{3}$  $\frac{3}{5}$

$3\frac{2}{3}$

The estimate of the sum
of my three numbers is 7.

**Glen**

The estimate of the sum
of my three numbers is 4.

**Huang**

1. What are three numbers Glen could have chosen?

   _____

2. What is the sum of those numbers?

   _____

3. What are three numbers Huang could have chosen?

   _____

4. What is the sum of those numbers?

   _____

# Fraction Distraction  5

Irene and Maria each chose three numbers
from the sign and estimated their sum.

$3\frac{2}{3}$   $5\frac{3}{5}$
$2\frac{1}{5}$
$3\frac{1}{6}$   $4\frac{7}{12}$
$\frac{11}{12}$

The estimate of the sum
of my three numbers is 8.

**Irene**

The estimate of the sum
of my three numbers is 13.

**Maria**

1. What are three numbers Irene could have chosen?

   _____

2. What is the sum of those numbers?

   _____

3. What are three numbers Maria could have chosen?

   _____

4. What is the sum of those numbers?

   _____

# Fraction Distraction  6

Kevin and Luis each chose three numbers from the sign and estimated their sum.

$1\frac{4}{7}$   $4\frac{3}{10}$

$8\frac{3}{7}$

$10\frac{2}{5}$   $5\frac{3}{5}$

$8\frac{1}{2}$

The estimate of the sum of my three numbers is 23.

**Kevin**

The estimate of the sum of my three numbers is 18.

**Luis**

1. What are three numbers Kevin could have chosen?

   _____

2. What is the sum of those numbers?

   _____

3. What are three numbers Luis could have chosen?

   _____

4. What is the sum of those numbers?

   _____

# Solutions

### Fraction Distraction  1

1. $3\frac{2}{3}, 2\frac{1}{2}, \frac{1}{5}$ or $3\frac{2}{3}, 2\frac{1}{2}, \frac{1}{3}$
2. $6\frac{11}{30}$ or $6\frac{1}{2}$
3. $1\frac{1}{4}, \frac{3}{4}, \frac{1}{5}$ or $1\frac{1}{4}, \frac{3}{4}, \frac{1}{3}$
4. $2\frac{1}{5}$ or $2\frac{1}{3}$

### Fraction Distraction 2

1. $\frac{3}{4}, \frac{1}{3}, \frac{1}{5}$ or $\frac{3}{5}, \frac{1}{3}, \frac{1}{5}$
2. $1\frac{17}{60}$ or $1\frac{2}{15}$
3. $2\frac{1}{12}, 1\frac{1}{2}, \frac{3}{4}$ or $2\frac{1}{12}, 1\frac{1}{2}, \frac{3}{5}$
4. $4\frac{1}{3}$ or $4\frac{11}{60}$

### Fraction Distraction 3

1. $2\frac{1}{8}, 1\frac{3}{4}, 1\frac{1}{3}$ or $2\frac{1}{8}, 1\frac{3}{4}, \frac{5}{8}$ or $2\frac{1}{8}, 1\frac{3}{4}, \frac{1}{2}$
2. $5\frac{5}{24}$ or $4\frac{1}{2}$ or $4\frac{3}{8}$
3. $1\frac{1}{3}, \frac{5}{8}, \frac{1}{4}$ or $1\frac{1}{3}, \frac{1}{2}, \frac{1}{4}$ or $\frac{5}{8}, \frac{1}{2}, \frac{1}{4}$
4. $2\frac{5}{24}$ or $2\frac{1}{12}$ or $1\frac{3}{8}$

### Fraction Distraction 4

1. $3\frac{2}{3}, 2\frac{1}{15}, \frac{4}{5}$ or $3\frac{2}{3}, 2\frac{1}{15}, \frac{3}{5}$ or $3\frac{2}{3}, 2\frac{1}{2}, \frac{1}{3}$
2. $6\frac{8}{15}$ or $6\frac{1}{3}$ or $6\frac{1}{2}$
3. $2\frac{1}{2}, \frac{4}{5}, \frac{1}{3}$ or $2\frac{1}{2}, \frac{3}{5}, \frac{1}{3}$ or $2\frac{1}{15}, \frac{4}{5}, \frac{3}{5}$
4. $3\frac{19}{30}$ or $3\frac{13}{30}$ or $3\frac{7}{15}$

### Fraction Distraction 5

1. $4\frac{7}{12}, 2\frac{1}{5}, \frac{11}{12}$ or $3\frac{2}{3}, 3\frac{1}{6}, \frac{11}{12}$
2. $7\frac{7}{10}$ or $7\frac{3}{4}$
3. $5\frac{3}{5}, 4\frac{7}{12}, 2\frac{1}{5}$ or $5\frac{3}{5}, 3\frac{2}{3}, 3\frac{1}{6}$
4. $12\frac{23}{60}$ or $12\frac{13}{30}$

### Fraction Distraction 6

1. $8\frac{1}{2}, 8\frac{3}{7}, 5\frac{3}{5}$ or $10\frac{2}{5}, 8\frac{1}{2}, 4\frac{3}{10}$
2. $22\frac{37}{70}$ or $23\frac{1}{5}$
3. $8\frac{3}{7}, 5\frac{3}{5}, 4\frac{3}{10}$ or $10\frac{2}{5}, 5\frac{3}{5}, 1\frac{4}{7}$
4. $18\frac{23}{70}$ or $17\frac{4}{7}$

# Best Buy

**Goals**
- Calculate unit costs.
- Use proportional reasoning to solve problems.
- Identify the greatest common factor (GCF) and the least common multiple (LCM) of three numbers.

**Notes**

Prior to doing this problem set, you may want to review the procedures for finding the greatest common factor (GCF) and the least common multiple (LCM) of three numbers. Point out to students how they can use the GCF or LCM to equate quantities. For each problem, three solution methods are given: one uses unit price, one uses the GCF of the three quantities, and one uses the LCM of the three quantities. Students could also solve by finding the GCF or LCM of the three costs and then comparing quantities, but that is not shown here.

**Solutions to all problems in this set appear on page 39.**

## Best Buy 1

**Questions to Ask**
- For Special A, what is the cost of 32 plates? ($60) How did you figure it out? (32 is 4 groups of 8, so the price of 32 plates is $4 \times \$15 = \$60$.)
- Which is the better buy, Special A or Special B? (B) Why? ($50 is less than $60 for the same number of plates.)
- If you want 16 plates, which is the better buy, Special B or Special C? (B) How did you figure it out? (For Special B, 16 is half of 32, so the price of 16 plates is $\frac{1}{2} \times \$50 = \$25$. For Special C, 16 is $\frac{1}{3}$ of 48, so the price of 16 plates is $\frac{1}{3} \times \$100$, or about $33.33.)

**Solutions**

1. Special B
2. Possible answers: Compare unit prices: Special A, about $1.88 per plate; Special B, about $1.56 per plate; Special C, about $2.08 per plate
Compare prices of 8 plates: Special A, $15; Special B, $12.50; Special C, about $16.67
Compare prices of 96 plates: Special A, $180; Special B, $150; Special C, $200

# Best Buy ⭐ 1

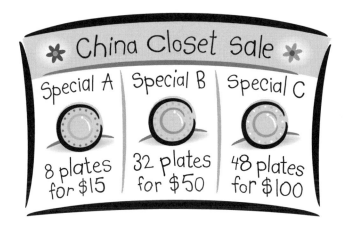

1. Which special is the best buy: A, B, or C?

   _____

2. Describe two ways to figure out the best buy.

   _____

   _____

   _____

   _____

# Best Buy ★ 2

1. Which type of bagel is the best buy?

   _____

2. Describe two ways to figure out the best buy.

   _____

   _____

   _____

   _____

# Best Buy ★ 3

1. Which type of apple is the best buy?

_____

2. Describe two ways to figure out the best buy.

_____

_____

_____

_____

# Best Buy  4

Along the Fairway

Fly-Long Golf Balls — 4 for $5.16

Swing Golf Balls — 16 for $22.00

On-Track Golf Balls — 24 for $32.96

1. Which brand of golf balls is the best buy?

_____

2. Describe two ways to figure out the best buy.

_____

_____

_____

_____

_____

# Best Buy  5

All-Natural Spring Water

Dewy
10 bottles for $6.90

Zippy
15 bottles for $10.80

Refresher
25 bottles for $16.25

1. Which brand of spring water is the best buy?

_____

2. Describe two ways to figure out the best buy.

_____

_____

_____

_____

_____

# Best Buy ★ 6

Muffins · Galore ·

Poppy Seed — 5 for $6.10

Walnut — 1¼ dozen for $22.50

Raisin — 20 for $29.00

**1.** Which type of muffin is the best buy?

_____

**2.** Describe two ways to figure out the best buy.

_____

_____

_____

_____

_____

# Solutions

## Best Buy  1

1. Special B

2. Possible answers: Compare
   unit prices: Special A, about
   $1.88 per plate; Special B,
   about $1.56 per plate;
   Special C, about $2.08
   per plate
   Compare prices of 8 plates:
   Special A, $15; Special B,
   $12.50; Special C, about $16.67
   Compare prices of 96 plates:
   Special A, $180; Special B,
   $150; Special C, $200

## Best Buy  2

1. Raisin bagels

2. Possible answers: Compare
   unit prices: Plain, about $0.67
   per bagel; Cinnamon, about
   $0.69 per bagel; Raisin, about
   $0.63 per bagel
   Compare prices of 3 bagels:
   Plain, about $2.00;
   Cinnamon, about $2.08;
   Raisin, about $1.88
   Compare prices of 36 bagels:
   Plain, $23.94; Cinnamon,
   $25.00; Raisin, $22.50

## Best Buy  3

1. Forkland apples

2. Possible answers: Compare
   unit prices: Sunnyday, about
   $0.71 per apple; Grandpop,
   $0.75 per apple; Forkland,
   about $0.67 per apple
   Compare prices of 3 apples:
   Sunnyday, about $2.13;
   Grandpop, $2.25;
   Forkland, $2.00
   Compare prices for 90 apples:
   Sunnyday, $63.75; Grandpop,
   $67.50; Forkland, $60.00

## Best Buy 4

1. Fly-Long Golf Balls

2. Possible answers: Compare
   unit prices: Fly-Long, $1.29 per
   golf ball; Swing, about $1.38
   per golf ball; On-Track, about
   $1.37 per golf ball
   Compare prices of 4 golf balls:
   Fly-Long, $5.16; Swing, $5.50;
   On-Track, about $5.49
   Compare prices of 48 golf
   balls: Fly-Long, $61.92; Swing,
   $66.00; On-Track, $65.92

## Best Buy 5

1. Refresher Spring Water

2. Possible answers: Compare
   unit prices: Dewy, $0.69 per
   bottle; Zippy, $0.72 per bottle;
   Refresher, $0.65 per bottle
   Compare prices of 5 bottles:
   Dewy, $3.45; Zippy, $3.60;
   Refresher, $3.25
   Compare prices of 150 bottles:
   Dewy, $103.50; Zippy, $108.00;
   Refresher, $97.50

## Best Buy 6

1. Poppy Seed

2. Possible answers: Compare
   unit prices: Poppy Seed, $1.22
   per muffin; Walnut, $1.50 per
   muffin; Raisin, $1.45 per muffin
   Compare prices of 5 muffins:
   Poppy Seed, $6.10; Walnut,
   $7.50; Raisin, $7.25
   Compare prices of 60 muffins:
   Poppy Seed, $73.20; Walnut,
   $90.00; Raisin, $87.00

# Ratio Roundup

**Goals**
- Generate equivalent ratios.
- Understand the phrase *for every*.
- Compute with percents.
- Use proportional reasoning to solve problems.

**Notes**

In all problems, the first person expresses a ratio as a percent and the second person expresses a ratio using the phrase *for every*. For students who have difficulty, suggest that they make drawings or use counters to model the problems. Each problem offers opportunities for students to construct more than the one solution method shown on the solutions page.

**Solutions to all problems in this set appear on page 47.**

### Ratio Roundup 1

**Questions to Ask**
- How many baseball cards does each boy have? (30)
- What types of baseball cards does each boy have? (National League and American League)
- What does Juan's ratio tell you about the number of each type of card he has? (For every 2 National League cards, he has 1 American League card.)
- How can you use this ratio to figure out the number of National League cards that Juan has? (In each group of 3 baseball cards, 2 of them are National League cards. Thirty cards are 10 groups of 3 cards, so Juan has $10 \times 2$, or 20 National League cards.)

**Solutions**
1. Juan
2. Eric: 60% of 30 cards = 18 National League cards
   Juan: In each group of 3 baseball cards, 2 are National League cards. 30 is 10 groups of 3, so Juan has $10 \times 2$, or 20 National League cards.

# Ratio Roundup  1

I have 30 National League and American League baseball cards. 60% of the cards are of players in the National League.

I have 30 baseball cards. For every 2 National League cards, I have 1 American League card.

**Eric**

**Juan**

1. Who has more National League cards? _____

2. How did you figure it out?

_____

_____

_____

_____

# Ratio Roundup ⭐ 2

I have 80 CDs. 25% of the CDs are country music. The rest are rock music.

In my collection of 80 CDs, I have 1 country CD for every 4 rock music CDs.

**Lisa**

**Kevin**

1.  Who has more country CDs? _____

2.  How did you figure it out?

_____

_____

_____

_____

# Ratio Roundup  3

I planted 60 tomato and pepper plants in my garden. 35% of the plants are peppers.

Of the 60 plants in my garden, I planted 2 pepper plants for every 3 tomato plants.

**Todd**

**Luis**

1. Who planted more pepper plants? _____

2. How did you figure it out?

_____

_____

_____

_____

# Ratio Roundup ⭐ 4

In a restaurant, I gave the server a 15% tip for a family meal that cost $60.

For a family meal that cost $60, I gave the server a tip of $1 for every $5 of the cost of the meal.

**Mr. Clark**

**Mrs. Handy**

1. Who gave the greater tip? _____

2. How did you figure it out?

_____

_____

_____

_____

# Ratio Roundup  5

There are 900 students in my school. 65% of them ride the bus.

There are 900 students in my school. For every 5 students who ride the bus, there are 4 students who get to school some other way.

**Keiko**

**Dan**

1. Whose school has more students who do **not** ride the bus?

_____

2. How did you figure it out?

_____

_____

_____

_____

# Ratio Roundup  6

On a field trip to the museum, 25% of the group were adults and the rest were students. A total of 56 people went on the field trip.

There were 56 people in my group on our field trip to the museum. For every 1 adult, there were 6 students.

**Maria**

**Chou**

1. Whose field trip had more students? _____

2. How did you figure it out?

_____

_____

_____

_____

# Solutions

### Ratio Roundup  1

1. Juan
2. Eric: 60% of 30 cards =
   18 National League cards
   Juan: In each group of 3 cards,
   2 are National League cards.
   30 is 10 groups of 3, so Juan
   has 10 × 2, or 20 National
   League cards.

### Ratio Roundup  2

1. Lisa
2. Lisa: 25% of 80 =
   20 country CDs
   Kevin: In each group of 5 CDs,
   1 is country music. 80 is
   16 groups of 5, so Kevin
   has 16 × 1, or 16 country CDs.

### Ratio Roundup 3

1. Luis
2. Todd: 35% of 60 =
   21 pepper plants
   Luis: In each group of 5 plants,
   2 are pepper plants. 60 is
   12 groups of 5, so Luis has
   12 × 2, or 24 pepper plants.

### Ratio Roundup 4

1. Mrs. Handy
2. Mr. Clark: 15% of $60 =
   $9 for the tip
   Mrs. Handy: For each group
   of $5, $1 is for a tip. $60
   is 12 groups of $5, so
   Mrs. Handy gave 12 × $1,
   or $12 for the tip.

### Ratio Roundup 5

1. Dan
2. Keiko: If 65% of the students
   ride the bus, then 35%
   do not. There are 35% of 900,
   or 315 students, at Keiko's
   school who do not ride
   the bus.
   Dan: In each group of
   9 students, 4 do not ride the
   bus. 900 is 100 groups of 9,
   so there are 100 × 4, or
   400 students at Dan's school
   who do not ride the bus.

### Ratio Roundup  6

1. Chou
2. Maria: If 25% of the people
   were adults, then 75% were
   students. 75% of 56, or
   42 students, were on Maria's
   field trip.
   Chou: In each group of
   7 people, 6 were students.
   56 is 8 groups of 7, so
   8 × 6, or 48 students, were
   on Chou's field trip.

# Number, Please!

**Goals**
- Identify factors and multiples of numbers.
- Identify the greatest common factor (GCF) and the least common multiple (LCM) of two or three numbers.
- Identify prime numbers.
- Use logical reasoning to solve problems.

**Notes**
Prior to doing this problem set, review odd and even numbers, prime numbers, multiples, least common multiple, factors, and greatest common factor of numbers. Point out that 0 is an even number and a multiple of all numbers.

**Solutions to all problems in this set appear on page 55.**

**Number, Please! 1**

**Questions to Ask**
- How many digits are in Bernard's number? (7)
- From Clue 1, what do you know about D? (It is 9, the GCF of 18, 27, and 36.)
- From Clue 4, what numbers are possible for B? (0 and 5) How do you know? (These are the only single-digit numbers that are multiples of 5.)
- From Clue 6, what do you know about E? (E is 0.)

**Solutions**
1. 7569018
2. Possible answer: From Clue 4, B is 0 or 5. From Clue 6, E is 0, so B is 5.

# Number, Please!  1

Bernard is thinking of a number.
The digits are represented by A, B, C, D, E, F, and G.
All of the digits are different.
Use the clues to figure out Bernard's number.

| | | | | | | |
|---|---|---|---|---|---|---|
| A | B | C | D | E | F | G |

## Clues

**1**  D is the greatest common factor of 18, 27, and 36.

**2**  G is the cube of 2.

**3**  F is a factor of all numbers.

**4**  B is a multiple of 5.

**5**  D − F − F = A

**6**  E + B = B

**7**  C is the least common multiple of 2 and 3.

1. What is Bernard's number? _____

2. Tell how you figured out the digit for B.

_____

_____

# Number, Please!  2

Conchita is thinking of a number.
The digits are represented by A, B, C, D, E, and F.
All of the digits are different.
Use the clues to figure out Conchita's number.

|  |  |  |  |  |  |
|---|---|---|---|---|---|
| __ | __ | __ | __ | __ | __ |
| A | B | C | D | E | F |

**Clues**

1  $A + F = A$

2  B and F are the only even numbers.

3  $C \div C = E$

4  $4 \times B + 1 = C$

5  $C - B = A$

6  $2B + E = D$

1. What is Conchita's number? _____

2. Tell how you figured out the digit for D.

_____

_____

# Number, Please! ⭐ 3

Dora is thinking of a number.
The digits are represented by A, B, C, D, E, and F.
All of the digits are different.
Use the clues to figure out Dora's number.

| A | B | C | D | E | F |
|---|---|---|---|---|---|

**Clues**

1  $A \times C = B$

2  $A \times D = A$

3  None of the digits is 0.

4  D and E are the only odd numbers.

5  $F = E \times A$

6  E is less than C.

1. What is Dora's number? _____

2. Tell how you figured out the digit for E.

_____

_____

# Number, Please!  4

Bruce is thinking of a number.
The digits are represented by A, B, C, D, E, F, and G.
All of the digits are different.
Use the clues to figure out Bruce's number.

| | | | | | | |
|---|---|---|---|---|---|---|
| ___ | ___ | ___ | ___ | ___ | ___ | ___ |
| A | B | C | D | E | F | G |

## Clues

**1** Only four of the digits are even numbers.

**2** A, D, and E are the only prime numbers.

**3** F + G = 14

**4** B + C = A

**5** A × B = A

**6** E < A < D

**7** E + 3 = A

**8** G is greater than F.

1. What is Bruce's number? _____

2. Tell how you figured out the digit for D.

_____

_____

# Number, Please!  5

Reyanne is thinking of a number.
The digits are represented by A, B, C, D, E, F, and G.
All of the digits are different.
Use the clues to figure out Reyanne's number.

| ___ | ___ | ___ | ___ | ___ | ___ | ___ |
|:---:|:---:|:---:|:---:|:---:|:---:|:---:|
| A | B | C | D | E | F | G |

## Clues

**1** A is the cube of a prime number.

**2** D has exactly 3 factors.

**3** The least common multiple of E and F is 30.

**4** C × E = E

**5** C + D = A + G

**6** B + C = 1

**7** D has one more factor than F.

1. What is Reyanne's number? _____

2. Tell how you figured out the digit for F.

_____

_____

# Number, Please!  6

Vance is thinking of a number.
The digits are represented by A, B, C, D, E, F, and G.
All of the digits are different.
Use the clues to figure out Vance's number.

| | | | | | | |
|---|---|---|---|---|---|---|
| A | B | C | D | E | F | G |

## Clues

**1** C, E, and G are prime numbers greater than 2.

**2** B, D, and F are the only even numbers.

**3** D = 2C

**4** A × D = D

**5** E is less than G.

**6** $\frac{1}{2}$B = F

**7** E + F = A + B

1. What is Vance's number? _____

2. Tell how you figured out the digit for F.

_____

_____

# Solutions

## Number, Please! 1

1. 7569018
2. Possible answer: From Clue 4, B is 0 or 5. From Clue 6, E is 0, so B is 5.

## Number, Please! 2

1. 729510
2. Possible answer: From Clue 1, F is zero. From Clue 2, B is even and not zero. From Clue 3, E is 1. From Clue 4, B is 2. From Clue 6, since B is 2, then D is 5.

## Number, Please! 3

1. 284136
2. Possible answer: From Clues 2 and 3, D is 1. From Clues 4 and 6, E can be only 3, 5, or 7. From Clue 5, since F must be a single-digit number, E must be 3.

## Number, Please! 4

1. 5147268
2. Possible answer: From Clue 2, A, D, and E are 2, 3, 5, or 7. From Clue 6, D is greater than A and A is greater than E, so D, A, and E can be 7, 5, and 3; 7, 5, and 2; 7, 3, and 2; or 5, 3, and 2. From Clue 7, E is 2 and A is 5, so D is 7.

## Number, Please! 5

1. 8019652
2. Possible answer: From Clue 3, E and F are 5 and 6 or 6 and 5. From Clues 2 and 7, F has only two factors, so F is 5.

## Number, Please! 6

1. 1836547
2. Possible answer: From Clue 1, C, E, and G are 3, 5, or 7. From Clue 4, A is 1. From Clue 3, D is 6 and C is 3. From Clue 5, E is 5 and G is 7. From Clues 2 and 6, if B is 4, then F is 2, or if B is 8, then F is 4. From Clue 7, 5 + F = 1 + B, so B is 8 and F is 4.

# Which Region?

**Goals**
- Identify factors, multiples, common factors, and common multiples of numbers.
- Identify odd, even, prime, composite, and square numbers.
- Interpret Venn diagrams that have three rings.
- Factor numbers in order to identify their prime factors.

**Notes**
Prior to doing this problem set, review the definitions of prime, composite, and square numbers and the prime factorization of numbers. Suggest to students that they list some numbers that are described by the labels of the sets before solving the problems. This may facilitate identification of the region locations for the given numbers.

**Solutions to all problems in this set appear on page 63.**

**Which Region? 1**

**Questions to Ask**
- How can you find the prime factors of a number? (Make a factor tree for the number. Factoring the factors until each factor cannot be factored further reveals all of the prime factors.)
- What are the prime factors of 12? (2 and 3)
- What are the prime factors of 210? (2, 3, 5, and 7)
- What belongs in region E? (numbers that are members of all three sets) What are the numbers? (5)
- What belongs in region C? (numbers that are factors of 140 but are not members of the other two sets) What are the numbers? (4, 10, 14, 20, 28, 35, 70, 140)

**Solutions**
1. B, E, D, C
2. Possible answer: 70 is a factor of 140 because 2 × 70 = 140. It is not a member of the other sets because the prime factors of 210 are 2, 3, 5, and 7, and the factors of 75 are 1, 3, 5, 15, 25, and 75, so 70 is in region C.

Name _____

# Which Region?  1

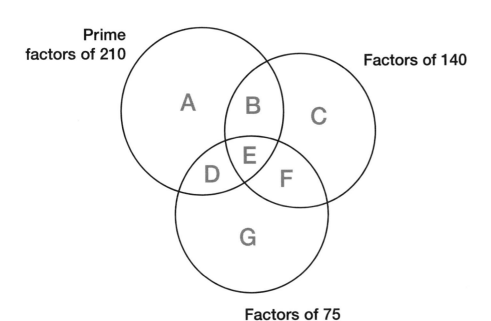

Prime factors of 210

Factors of 140

Factors of 75

1. Identify the region each number is in.

   7 is in region _____.

   5 is in region _____.

   3 is in region _____.

   70 is in region _____.

2. Tell how you figured out the region 70 is in.

   _____

   _____

# Which Region?  2

Common multiples
of 2 and 5

A

B

C

Common multiples
of 3 and 4

E

D

F

G

Common multiples of 3 and 5

1. Identify the region each number is in.

    24 is in region _____.

    60 is in region _____.

    30 is in region _____.

    120 is in region _____.

2. Tell how you figured out the region 120 is in.

    _____

    _____

Reasoning with Numbers

# Which Region?

Common multiples
of 2 and 3

A

B

Common factors
of 24 and 36

C

D

E

F

G

Multiples of 4

1. Identify the region each number is in.

   6 is in region _____.

   64 is in region _____.

   0 is in region _____.

   12 is in region _____.

2. Tell how you figured out the region 12 is in.

   _____

   _____

# Which Region?  4

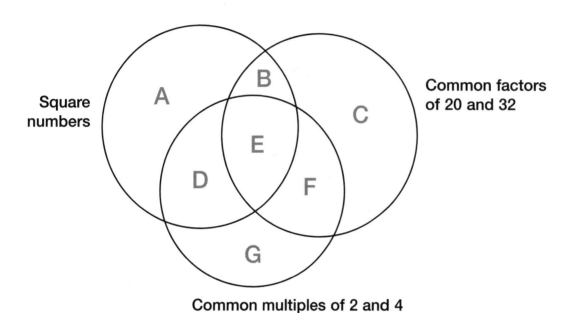

**Square numbers**

**Common factors of 20 and 32**

A

B

C

E

D

F

G

**Common multiples of 2 and 4**

1. Identify the region each number is in.

   4 is in region _____.

   16 is in region _____.

   48 is in region _____.

   100 is in region _____.

2. Tell how you figured out the region 100 is in.

   _____

   _____

# Which Region?  5

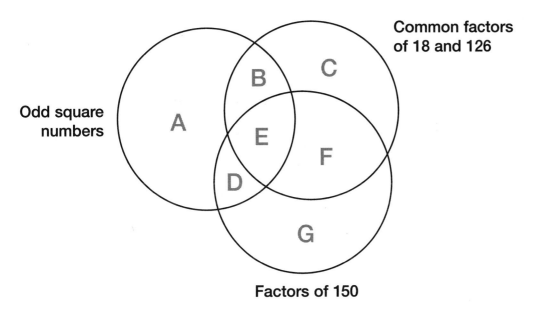

Common factors
of 18 and 126

Odd square
numbers

A  B  C
E  F
D
G

Factors of 150

1. Identify the region each number is in.

    9 is in region _____.

    25 is in region _____.

    75 is in region _____.

    49 is in region _____.

2. Tell how you figured out the region 49 is in.

    _____

    _____

# Which Region?  6

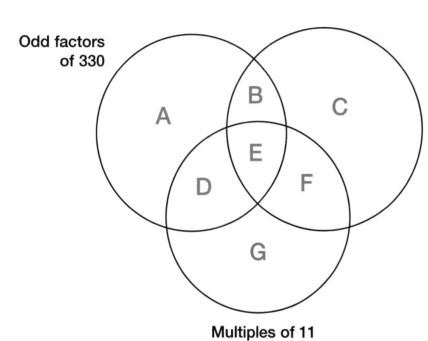

Odd factors
of 330

A   B   C   Composite numbers

E

D   F

G

Multiples of 11

**1.** Identify the region each number is in.

1 is in region _____.

66 is in region _____.

0 is in region _____.

165 is in region _____.

**2.** Tell how you figured out the region 165 is in.

_____

_____

Reasoning with Numbers

# Solutions

### Which Region?  1

1. B, E, D, C

2. Possible answer: 70 is a factor of 140 because 2 × 70 = 140. It is not a member of the other sets because the prime factors of 210 are 2, 3, 5, and 7, and the factors of 75 are 1, 3, 5, 15, 25, and 75, so 70 is in region C.

### Which Region?  2

1. C, E, D, E

2. Possible answer: Common multiples of 2 and 5 are multiples of 10; 120 is a multiple of 10. Common multiples of 3 and 4 are multiples of 12; 120 is a multiple of 12. Common multiples of 3 and 5 are multiples of 15; 120 is a multiple of 15, so 120 is in region E.

### Which Region?  3

1. B, G, D, E

2. Possible answer: The common multiples of 3 and 2 are all multiples of 6; 12 is a multiple of 6. 12 is a common factor of both 24 and 36, and it is a multiple of 4, so 12 is in region E.

### Which Region?  4

1. E, D, G, D

2. Possible answer: 100 is not a factor of 20 and 32. 100 is a square number because 10 × 10 = 100. Common multiples of 2 and 4 are all multiples of 4. 100 is a multiple of 4, so 100 is in region D.

### Which Region?  5

1. B, D, G, A

2. Possible answer: 49 is an odd number and it is the square of 7. It is not a common factor of 18 and 126 and it is not a factor of 150, so 49 is in region A.

### Which Region?  6

1. A, F, G, E

2. Possible answer: 165 is a factor of 330 because 2 × 165 = 330. 165 is a composite number because it has more than two factors. 165 is a multiple of 11 because 15 × 11 = 165, so 165 is in region E.

# Beanbag Toss

**Goals**
- Find sums with multiple addends.
- Identify sets of numbers that add to a given sum.
- Use logical reasoning to solve problems.

**Notes**

Encourage students to explain their thinking. For example, to use the least number of beanbags to score 100 in Beanbag Toss 1, students may try as many 19s as possible and see if the other numbers can make the difference. If not, then they have to try using one fewer 19, and so on. Encourage students to find as many alternate solutions as they can whenever a possible answer is given on the solutions page.

**Solutions to all problems in this set appear on page 71.**

**Beanbag Toss 1**

**Questions to Ask**
- What score do you want to get? (100)
- Can you score 100 with 5 beanbags? (no) Why not? (19 is the greatest ring number and $5 \times 19$ is less than 100.)
- What do you think is the least number of beanbags you need to get 100? (6)
- What do you think is the greatest number of beanbags you need to get 100? (12) Why? (9 is the lowest ring number and $12 \times 9$ is the first product greater than 100.)

**Solutions**
1. 6
2. Possible answer: $4 \times 19 + 11 + 13 = 100$
3. 10
4. Possible answer: $5 \times 9 + 5 \times 11 = 100$
5. Yes; Possible answer: $2 \times 9 + 3 \times 11 + 13 + 17 + 19 = 100$

# Beanbag Toss  1

In Beanbag Toss, you toss some number of beanbags. All of your beanbags land on the target. Your score is the total of your ring numbers.

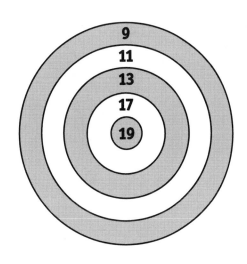

You want to score exactly 100.

1. What is the least number of beanbags you could toss?

   _____

2. Where would they land?

   _____

3. What is the greatest number of beanbags you could toss?

   _____

4. Where would they land?

   _____

5. Can your beanbags land in all five rings?
   If so, where would they land?

   _____

# Beanbag Toss ★ 2

In Beanbag Toss, you toss some
number of beanbags. All of your
beanbags land on the target.
Your score is the total of your
ring numbers.

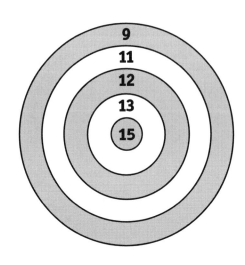

You want to score exactly 90.

1. What is the least number of beanbags you could toss?

   _____

2. Where would they land?

   _____

3. What is the greatest number of beanbags you could toss?

   _____

4. Where would they land?

   _____

5. Can your beanbags land in all five rings?
   If so, where would they land?

   _____

# Beanbag Toss ⭐ 3

In Beanbag Toss, you toss some
number of beanbags. All of your
beanbags land on the target.
Your score is the total of your
ring numbers.

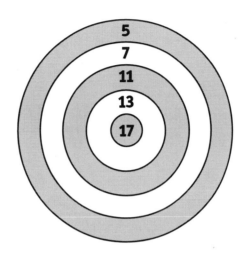

You want to score exactly 80.

1. What is the least number of beanbags you could toss?

   _____

2. Where would they land?

   _____

3. What is the greatest number of beanbags you could toss?

   _____

4. Where would they land?

   _____

5. Can your beanbags land in all five rings?
   If so, where would they land?

   _____

# Beanbag Toss

In Beanbag Toss, you toss some number of beanbags. All of your beanbags land on the target. Your score is the total of your ring numbers.

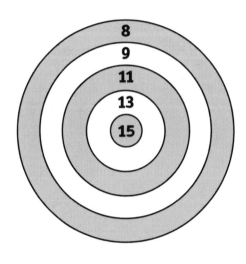

You want to score exactly 75.

1. What is the least number of beanbags you could toss?

   _____

2. Where would they land?

   _____

3. What is the greatest number of beanbags you could toss?

   _____

4. Where would they land?

   _____

5. Can your beanbags land in all five rings?
   If so, where would they land?

   _____

# Beanbag Toss 5

In Beanbag Toss, you toss some number of beanbags. All of your beanbags land on the target. Your score is the total of your ring numbers.

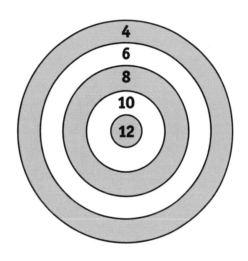

You want to score exactly 50.

1. What is the least number of beanbags you could toss?

   _____

2. Where would they land?

   _____

3. What is the greatest number of beanbags you could toss?

   _____

4. Where would they land?

   _____

5. Can your beanbags land in all five rings?
   If so, where would they land?

   _____

# Beanbag Toss  6

In Beanbag Toss, you toss some number of beanbags. All of your beanbags land on the target. Your score is the total of your ring numbers.

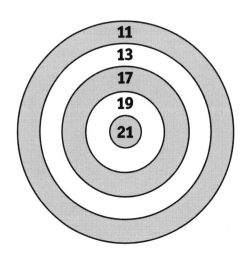

You want to score exactly 120.

1. What is the least number of beanbags you could toss?

_____

2. Where would they land?

_____

3. What is the greatest number of beanbags you could toss?

_____

4. Where would they land?

_____

5. Can your beanbags land in all five rings?
   If so, where would they land?

_____

# Solutions

### Beanbag Toss 1

1. 6
2. Possible answer:
   $4 \times 19 + 11 + 13 = 100$
3. 10
4. Possible answer:
   $5 \times 9 + 5 \times 11 = 100$
5. Yes; Possible answer: $2 \times 9 + 3 \times 11 + 13 + 17 + 19 = 100$

### Beanbag Toss 2

1. 6
2. $6 \times 15 = 90$
3. 10
4. $10 \times 9 = 90$
5. Yes; Possible answer: $9 + 11 + 12 + 13 + 3 \times 15 = 90$

### Beanbag Toss 3

1. 6
2. Possible answer:
   $2 \times 17 + 3 \times 13 + 7 = 80$
3. 16
4. $16 \times 5 = 80$
5. Yes; Possible answer: $5 + 3 \times 7 + 11 + 2 \times 13 + 17 = 80$

### Beanbag Toss 4

1. 5
2. $5 \times 15 = 75$
3. 9
4. Possible answer:
   $8 \times 8 + 11 = 75$
5. Yes; Possible answer: $2 \times 8 + 9 + 2 \times 11 + 13 + 15 = 75$

### Beanbag Toss 5

1. 5
2. Possible answer:
   $3 \times 12 + 8 + 6 = 50$
3. 12
4. Possible answer:
   $11 \times 4 + 6 = 50$
5. Yes; Possible answer: $2 \times 4 + 2 \times 6 + 8 + 10 + 12 = 50$

### Beanbag Toss 6

1. 6
2. Possible answer:
   $3 \times 19 + 3 \times 21 = 120$
3. 10
4. Possible answer:
   $5 \times 11 + 5 \times 13 = 120$
5. Yes; Possible answer: $11 + 4 \times 13 + 17 + 19 + 21 = 120$

# Fraction Squares

**Goals**
- Multiply and divide with fractions.
- Simplify fractions.
- Use inverse operations to solve problems.

**Notes**
Prior to doing this problem set, review the procedures for simplifying fractions and for converting between improper fractions and mixed numbers.

Solutions to all problems in this set appear on page 79.

**Fraction Squares 1**

**Questions to Ask**
- What is the row rule? (Multiply by $\frac{2}{3}$ going across.)
- What is the column rule? (Multiply by $\frac{1}{6}$ going up.)
- What number is above $\frac{1}{2}$? ($\frac{1}{12}$) How do you know?
  ($\frac{1}{2} \times \frac{1}{6} = \frac{1}{12}$)
- What number is to the right of 3? (2) How do you know?
  ($3 \times \frac{2}{3} = \frac{3}{1} \times \frac{2}{3} = \frac{6}{3} = 2$)
- What number is below 3? (18) How do you know?
  ($3 \div \frac{1}{6} = 3 \times \frac{6}{1} = 18$)

**Solutions**

1.

| | | | |
|---|---|---|---|
| $\frac{1}{8}$ | $\frac{1}{12}$ | $\frac{1}{18}$ | $\frac{1}{27}$ |
| $\frac{3}{4}$ | $\frac{1}{2}$ | $\frac{1}{3}$ | $\frac{2}{9}$ |
| $4\frac{1}{2}$ | $3$ | $2$ | $1\frac{1}{3}$ |
| $27$ | $18$ | $12$ | $8$ |

$\times \frac{1}{6}$ (up the left side)

$\longrightarrow \times \frac{2}{3}$

2. Possible answer: The number above $\frac{1}{2}$ is $\frac{1}{2} \times \frac{1}{6} = \frac{1}{12}$.
Then the number to the right of $\frac{1}{12}$ is $\frac{1}{12} \times \frac{2}{3} = \frac{2}{36} = \frac{1}{18}$.

# Fraction Squares  1

Record all fractions in simplest form.

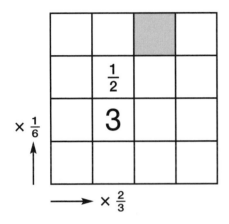

1. Complete the fraction square.

   • Multiply by $\frac{2}{3}$ going across.

   • Multiply by $\frac{1}{6}$ going up.

2. How did you figure out the number in the shaded square?

   _____

   _____

   _____

# Fraction Squares 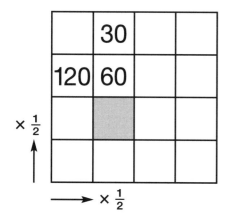 2 ★

Record all fractions in simplest form.

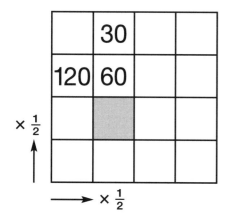

$\times \frac{1}{2}$

$\longrightarrow \times \frac{1}{2}$

1. Complete the fraction square.

   • Multiply by $\frac{1}{2}$ going across.

   • Multiply by $\frac{1}{2}$ going up.

2. How did you figure out the number in the shaded square?

   _____

   _____

   _____

# Fraction Squares  3

Record all fractions in simplest form.

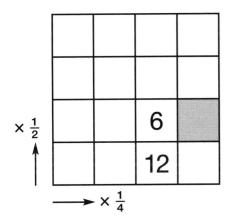

1. Complete the fraction square.

   • Multiply by $\frac{1}{4}$ going across.

   • Multiply by $\frac{1}{2}$ going up.

2. How did you figure out the number in the shaded square?

   _____

   _____

   _____

# Fraction Squares ★ 4

Record all fractions in simplest form.

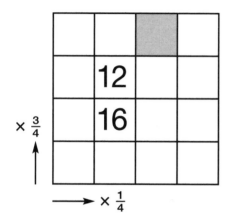

1. Complete the fraction square.

   • Multiply by $\frac{1}{4}$ going across.

   • Multiply by $\frac{3}{4}$ going up.

2. How did you figure out the number in the shaded square?

   _____

   _____

   _____

# Fraction Squares  5

Record all fractions in simplest form.

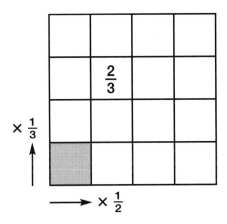

1. Complete the fraction square.

   • Multiply by $\frac{1}{2}$ going across.
   • Multiply by $\frac{1}{3}$ going up.

2. How did you figure out the number in the shaded square?

   _____

   _____

   _____

# Fraction Squares ⭐ 6

Record all fractions in simplest form.

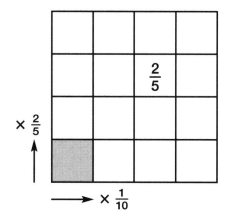

1. Complete the fraction square.

   • Multiply by $\frac{1}{10}$ going across.

   • Multiply by $\frac{2}{5}$ going up.

2. How did you figure out the number in the shaded square?

   _____

   _____

   _____

Reasoning with Numbers

# Solutions

## Fraction Squares 1

1.

| $\frac{1}{8}$ | $\frac{1}{12}$ | $\frac{1}{18}$ | $\frac{1}{27}$ |
|---|---|---|---|
| $\frac{3}{4}$ | $\frac{1}{2}$ | $\frac{1}{3}$ | $\frac{2}{9}$ |
| $4\frac{1}{2}$ | $3$ | $2$ | $1\frac{1}{3}$ |
| $27$ | $18$ | $12$ | $8$ |

$\times \frac{1}{6}$ (left column) → $\times \frac{2}{3}$

2. Possible answer: The number above $\frac{1}{2}$ is $\frac{1}{2} \times \frac{1}{6} = \frac{1}{12}$. Then the number to the right of $\frac{1}{12}$ is $\frac{1}{12} \times \frac{2}{3} = \frac{2}{36} = \frac{1}{18}$.

## Fraction Squares 2

1.

| $60$ | $30$ | $15$ | $7\frac{1}{2}$ |
|---|---|---|---|
| $120$ | $60$ | $30$ | $15$ |
| $240$ | $120$ | $60$ | $30$ |
| $480$ | $240$ | $120$ | $60$ |

$\times \frac{1}{2}$ (left column) → $\times \frac{1}{2}$

2. Possible answer: The number below 60 is $60 \times \frac{2}{1} = 120$.

## Fraction Squares 3

1.

| $24$ | $6$ | $1\frac{1}{2}$ | $\frac{3}{8}$ |
|---|---|---|---|
| $48$ | $12$ | $3$ | $\frac{3}{4}$ |
| $96$ | $24$ | $6$ | $1\frac{1}{2}$ |
| $192$ | $48$ | $12$ | $3$ |

$\times \frac{1}{2}$ (left column) → $\times \frac{1}{4}$

2. Possible answer: The number to the right of 6 is $6 \times \frac{1}{4} = \frac{6}{4} = 1\frac{2}{4} = 1\frac{1}{2}$.

## Fraction Squares 4

1.

| $36$ | $9$ | $2\frac{1}{4}$ | $\frac{9}{16}$ |
|---|---|---|---|
| $48$ | $12$ | $3$ | $\frac{3}{4}$ |
| $64$ | $16$ | $4$ | $1$ |
| $85\frac{1}{3}$ | $21\frac{1}{3}$ | $5\frac{1}{3}$ | $1\frac{1}{3}$ |

$\times \frac{3}{4}$ (left column) → $\times \frac{1}{4}$

2. Possible answer: The number to the right of 12 is $12 \times \frac{1}{4} = 3$. Then the number above 3 is $3 \times \frac{3}{4} = \frac{9}{4} = 2\frac{1}{4}$.

## Fraction Squares 5

1.

| $\frac{4}{9}$ | $\frac{2}{9}$ | $\frac{1}{9}$ | $\frac{1}{18}$ |
|---|---|---|---|
| $1\frac{1}{3}$ | $\frac{2}{3}$ | $\frac{1}{3}$ | $\frac{1}{6}$ |
| $4$ | $2$ | $1$ | $\frac{1}{2}$ |
| $12$ | $6$ | $3$ | $1\frac{1}{2}$ |

$\times \frac{1}{3}$ (left column) → $\times \frac{1}{2}$

2. Possible answer: The number below $\frac{2}{3}$ is $\frac{2}{3} \times \frac{3}{1} = 2$. The number below 2 is $2 \times \frac{3}{1} = 6$. Then the number to the left of 6 is $6 \times \frac{2}{1} = 12$.

## Fraction Squares 6

1.

| $16$ | $1\frac{3}{5}$ | $\frac{4}{25}$ | $\frac{1}{125}$ |
|---|---|---|---|
| $40$ | $4$ | $\frac{2}{5}$ | $\frac{1}{25}$ |
| $100$ | $10$ | $1$ | $\frac{1}{10}$ |
| $250$ | $25$ | $2\frac{1}{2}$ | $\frac{1}{4}$ |

$\times \frac{2}{5}$ (left column) → $\times \frac{1}{10}$

2. Possible answer: The number below $\frac{2}{5}$ is $\frac{2}{5} \times \frac{5}{2} = 1$. The number below 1 is $1 \times \frac{5}{2} = 2\frac{1}{2}$. The number to the left of $2\frac{1}{2}$ is $2\frac{1}{2} \times \frac{10}{1} = 25$. Then the number to the left of 25 is $25 \times \frac{10}{1} = 250$.

# Grid Sums

**Goals**
- Find sums and missing addends.
- Compute with fractions.
- Use logical reasoning to solve problems.

**Notes**
Encourage students to start with any row or column that has only one empty rectangle. Remind students to express the sum or missing addend in simplest form. After students have completed each grid, have them verify that the row and column numbers produce the circle sums.

**Solutions to all problems in this set appear on page 87.**

### Grid Sums 1

**Questions to Ask**
- What is the sum of the numbers in Row 1? ($2\frac{2}{5}$)
- What number belongs in the empty rectangle in Row 1? ($\frac{4}{5}$) How do you know? ($2\frac{2}{5} - \frac{2}{5} - \frac{1}{2} - \frac{7}{10} = \frac{4}{5}$)
- What is the sum of the numbers in Column 2? ($1\frac{2}{5}$)
- What number belongs in the empty rectangle in Column 2? ($\frac{3}{10}$) How do you know? ($1\frac{2}{5} - \frac{1}{2} - \frac{1}{10} - \frac{1}{2} = \frac{3}{10}$)
- What is the sum of the numbers in Row 3? ($1\frac{9}{10}$) How do you know? ($\frac{1}{2} + \frac{3}{10} + \frac{9}{10} + \frac{1}{5} = \frac{19}{10} = 1\frac{9}{10}$)

**Solutions**

1.

| | | | | |
|---|---|---|---|---|
| **Row 1** | $\frac{2}{5}$ | $\frac{1}{2}$ | $\frac{4}{5}$ | $\frac{7}{10}$ | $\left(2\frac{2}{5}\right)$ |
| **Row 2** | $\frac{1}{5}$ | $\frac{1}{10}$ | $\frac{2}{5}$ | $\frac{1}{10}$ | $\left(\frac{4}{5}\right)$ |
| **Row 3** | $\frac{1}{2}$ | $\frac{3}{10}$ | $\frac{9}{10}$ | $\frac{1}{5}$ | $\left(1\frac{9}{10}\right)$ |
| **Row 4** | $\frac{7}{10}$ | $\frac{1}{2}$ | $\frac{1}{5}$ | $\frac{3}{5}$ | $(2)$ |

$\left(1\frac{4}{5}\right)$ $\left(1\frac{2}{5}\right)$ $\left(2\frac{3}{10}\right)$ $\left(1\frac{3}{5}\right)$

2. $7\frac{1}{10}$

3. $7\frac{1}{10}$

4. yes

# Grid Sums  1

Numbers in circles are sums of rows and columns.

**1.** Fill the empty squares and the empty circles.

|        | | | | | |
|--------|---|---|---|---|---|
| Row 1 | $\frac{2}{5}$ | $\frac{1}{2}$ | | $\frac{7}{10}$ | $\left(2\frac{2}{5}\right)$ |
| Row 2 | $\frac{1}{5}$ | $\frac{1}{10}$ | | $\frac{1}{10}$ | ( ) |
| Row 3 | $\frac{1}{2}$ | | $\frac{9}{10}$ | $\frac{1}{5}$ | ( ) |
| Row 4 | | $\frac{1}{2}$ | $\frac{1}{5}$ | | ( 2 ) |
|  | $\left(1\frac{4}{5}\right)$ | $\left(1\frac{2}{5}\right)$ | $\left(2\frac{3}{10}\right)$ | $\left(1\frac{3}{5}\right)$ | |

**2.** What is the sum of the numbers that are the row sums?

_____

**3.** What is the sum of the numbers that are the column sums?

_____

**4.** Are the two sums the same? _____

# Grid Sums  ★2

Numbers in circles are sums of rows and columns.

1.  Fill the empty squares and the empty circles.

| | | | | |
|---|---|---|---|---|
| **Row 1** | | $\frac{1}{10}$ | $\frac{2}{5}$ | $\frac{3}{5}$ | $\left(1\frac{1}{5}\right)$ |
| **Row 2** | $\frac{1}{2}$ | $\frac{1}{5}$ | $\frac{7}{10}$ | | $\left(1\frac{9}{10}\right)$ |
| **Row 3** | $\frac{3}{10}$ | $\frac{2}{5}$ | | | $\left(\frac{9}{10}\right)$ |
| **Row 4** | $\frac{2}{5}$ | $\frac{2}{5}$ | $\frac{1}{10}$ | | $\left(1\frac{1}{10}\right)$ |
| | $\bigcirc$ | $\bigcirc$ | $\left(1\frac{3}{10}\right)$ | $\left(1\frac{2}{5}\right)$ | |

2.  What is the sum of the numbers that are the row sums?

    _____

3.  What is the sum of the numbers that are the column sums?

    _____

4.  Are the two sums the same? _____

# Grid Sums ⭐ 3

Numbers in circles are sums of rows and columns.

**1.** Fill the empty squares and the empty circles.

| | | | | |
|---|---|---|---|---|
| **Row 1** | $\frac{4}{5}$ | $\frac{1}{10}$ | $\frac{3}{10}$ | $\frac{7}{10}$ | ◯ |
| **Row 2** | | | $\frac{1}{10}$ | | $1\frac{3}{10}$ |
| **Row 3** | | $\frac{1}{10}$ | $\frac{1}{5}$ | $\frac{3}{5}$ | $1\frac{1}{2}$ |
| **Row 4** | $\frac{4}{5}$ | | | $\frac{4}{5}$ | $2\frac{1}{10}$ |

$2\frac{3}{5}$    ◯    $1$    $2\frac{3}{5}$

**2.** What is the sum of the numbers that are the row sums?

_____

**3.** What is the sum of the numbers that are the column sums?

_____

**4.** Are the two sums the same? _____

# Grid Sums  4

Numbers in circles are sums of rows and columns.

1. Fill the empty squares and the empty circles.

| | | | | |
|---|---|---|---|---|
| Row 1 | $\frac{3}{5}$ | | $\frac{9}{10}$ | $\frac{3}{4}$ | $\left(2\frac{11}{20}\right)$ |
| Row 2 | $\frac{9}{10}$ | | | $\frac{9}{20}$ | $\bigcirc$ |
| Row 3 | $1\frac{1}{20}$ | $\frac{3}{20}$ | $\frac{3}{20}$ | $\frac{9}{20}$ | $\bigcirc$ |
| Row 4 | | $1\frac{1}{5}$ | $1\frac{1}{5}$ | | $\left(4\frac{1}{20}\right)$ |

$\left(3\frac{3}{20}\right)$ $\left(2\frac{1}{4}\right)$ $\left(2\frac{11}{20}\right)$ $\left(2\frac{7}{10}\right)$

2. What is the sum of the numbers that are the row sums?

_____

3. What is the sum of the numbers that are the column sums?

_____

4. Are the two sums the same? _____

Computation

# Grid Sums ★ 5

Numbers in circles are sums of rows and columns.

**1.** Fill the empty squares and the empty circles.

| | | | | | |
|---|---|---|---|---|---|
| **Row 1** | $\frac{1}{2}$ | | $\frac{1}{8}$ | | $\left(1\frac{5}{8}\right)$ |
| **Row 2** | $1\frac{1}{8}$ | $0$ | | $1$ | $\left(2\frac{5}{8}\right)$ |
| **Row 3** | $\frac{5}{8}$ | $\frac{1}{4}$ | $\frac{1}{4}$ | $\frac{3}{4}$ | $\bigcirc$ |
| **Row 4** | | $\frac{1}{8}$ | $\frac{3}{8}$ | $\frac{7}{8}$ | $\left(2\frac{3}{8}\right)$ |

$\left(3\frac{1}{4}\right)$ $\bigcirc$ $\bigcirc$ $\left(3\frac{1}{4}\right)$

**2.** What is the sum of the numbers that are the row sums?

_____

**3.** What is the sum of the numbers that are the column sums?

_____

**4.** Are the two sums the same? _____

Reasoning with Numbers

# Grid Sums ★ 6

Numbers in circles are sums of rows and columns.

**1.** Fill the empty squares and the empty circles.

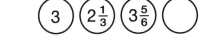

|  |  |  |  |  |  |
|---|---|---|---|---|---|
| **Row 1** | $\frac{2}{3}$ |  | $1\frac{1}{3}$ | $1\frac{1}{6}$ | ④ |
| **Row 2** |  | $\frac{5}{6}$ | $\frac{1}{3}$ | $1$ | $3\frac{1}{3}$ |
| **Row 3** | $\frac{5}{6}$ | $\frac{1}{2}$ |  | $\frac{1}{3}$ | $3\frac{1}{6}$ |
| **Row 4** |  |  |  | $\frac{1}{6}$ | ○ |
|  | ③ | $2\frac{1}{3}$ | $3\frac{5}{6}$ | ○ |  |

**2.** What is the sum of the numbers that are the row sums?

_____

**3.** What is the sum of the numbers that are the column sums?

_____

**4.** Are the two sums the same? _____

# Solutions

### Grid Sums 1

1.

| | | | | |
|---|---|---|---|---|
| Row 1 | $\frac{2}{5}$ | $\frac{1}{2}$ | $\frac{4}{5}$ | $\frac{7}{10}$ | $\left(2\frac{2}{5}\right)$ |
| Row 2 | $\frac{1}{5}$ | $\frac{1}{10}$ | $\frac{2}{5}$ | $\frac{1}{10}$ | $\left(\frac{4}{5}\right)$ |
| Row 3 | $\frac{1}{2}$ | $\frac{3}{10}$ | $\frac{9}{10}$ | $\frac{1}{5}$ | $\left(1\frac{9}{10}\right)$ |
| Row 4 | $\frac{7}{10}$ | $\frac{1}{2}$ | $\frac{1}{5}$ | $\frac{3}{5}$ | $(2)$ |

$\left(1\frac{4}{5}\right)\left(1\frac{2}{5}\right)\left(2\frac{3}{10}\right)\left(1\frac{3}{5}\right)$

2. $7\frac{1}{10}$
3. $7\frac{1}{10}$
4. yes

### Grid Sums 2 ★

1.

| | | | | |
|---|---|---|---|---|
| Row 1 | $\frac{1}{10}$ | $\frac{1}{10}$ | $\frac{2}{5}$ | $\frac{3}{5}$ | $\left(1\frac{1}{5}\right)$ |
| Row 2 | $\frac{1}{2}$ | $\frac{1}{5}$ | $\frac{7}{10}$ | $\frac{1}{2}$ | $\left(1\frac{9}{10}\right)$ |
| Row 3 | $\frac{3}{10}$ | $\frac{2}{5}$ | $\frac{1}{10}$ | $\frac{1}{10}$ | $\left(\frac{9}{10}\right)$ |
| Row 4 | $\frac{2}{5}$ | $\frac{2}{5}$ | $\frac{1}{10}$ | $\frac{1}{5}$ | $\left(1\frac{1}{10}\right)$ |

$\left(1\frac{3}{10}\right)\left(1\frac{1}{10}\right)\left(1\frac{3}{10}\right)\left(1\frac{2}{5}\right)$

2. $5\frac{1}{10}$
3. $5\frac{1}{10}$
4. yes

### Grid Sums 3 ★

1.

| | | | | |
|---|---|---|---|---|
| Row 1 | $\frac{4}{5}$ | $\frac{1}{10}$ | $\frac{3}{10}$ | $\frac{7}{10}$ | $\left(1\frac{9}{10}\right)$ |
| Row 2 | $\frac{2}{5}$ | $\frac{3}{10}$ | $\frac{1}{10}$ | $\frac{1}{2}$ | $\left(1\frac{3}{10}\right)$ |
| Row 3 | $\frac{3}{5}$ | $\frac{1}{10}$ | $\frac{1}{5}$ | $\frac{3}{5}$ | $\left(1\frac{1}{2}\right)$ |
| Row 4 | $\frac{4}{5}$ | $\frac{1}{10}$ | $\frac{2}{5}$ | $\frac{4}{5}$ | $\left(2\frac{1}{10}\right)$ |

$\left(2\frac{3}{5}\right)\left(\frac{3}{5}\right)\left(1\right)\left(2\frac{3}{5}\right)$

2. $6\frac{4}{5}$
3. $6\frac{4}{5}$
4. yes

### Grid Sums 4 ★

1.

| | | | | |
|---|---|---|---|---|
| Row 1 | $\frac{3}{5}$ | $\frac{3}{10}$ | $\frac{9}{10}$ | $\frac{3}{4}$ | $\left(2\frac{11}{20}\right)$ |
| Row 2 | $\frac{9}{10}$ | $\frac{3}{5}$ | $\frac{3}{10}$ | $\frac{9}{20}$ | $\left(2\frac{1}{4}\right)$ |
| Row 3 | $1\frac{1}{20}$ | $\frac{3}{20}$ | $\frac{3}{20}$ | $\frac{9}{20}$ | $\left(1\frac{4}{5}\right)$ |
| Row 4 | $\frac{3}{5}$ | $1\frac{1}{5}$ | $1\frac{1}{5}$ | $1\frac{1}{10}$ | $\left(4\frac{1}{20}\right)$ |

$\left(3\frac{3}{20}\right)\left(2\frac{1}{4}\right)\left(2\frac{11}{20}\right)\left(2\frac{7}{10}\right)$

2. $10\frac{13}{20}$
3. $10\frac{13}{20}$
4. yes

### Grid Sums 5 ★

1.

| | | | | |
|---|---|---|---|---|
| Row 1 | $\frac{1}{2}$ | $\frac{3}{8}$ | $\frac{1}{8}$ | $\frac{5}{8}$ | $\left(1\frac{5}{8}\right)$ |
| Row 2 | $1\frac{1}{8}$ | $0$ | $\frac{1}{2}$ | $1$ | $\left(2\frac{5}{8}\right)$ |
| Row 3 | $\frac{5}{8}$ | $\frac{1}{4}$ | $\frac{1}{4}$ | $\frac{3}{4}$ | $\left(1\frac{7}{8}\right)$ |
| Row 4 | $1$ | $\frac{1}{8}$ | $\frac{3}{8}$ | $\frac{7}{8}$ | $\left(2\frac{3}{8}\right)$ |

$\left(3\frac{1}{4}\right)\left(\frac{3}{4}\right)\left(1\frac{1}{4}\right)\left(3\frac{1}{4}\right)$

2. $8\frac{1}{2}$
3. $8\frac{1}{2}$
4. yes

### Grid Sums 6 ★

1.

| | | | | |
|---|---|---|---|---|
| Row 1 | $\frac{2}{3}$ | $\frac{5}{6}$ | $1\frac{1}{3}$ | $1\frac{1}{6}$ | $(4)$ |
| Row 2 | $1\frac{1}{6}$ | $\frac{5}{6}$ | $\frac{1}{3}$ | $1$ | $\left(3\frac{1}{3}\right)$ |
| Row 3 | $\frac{5}{6}$ | $\frac{1}{2}$ | $1\frac{1}{2}$ | $\frac{1}{3}$ | $\left(3\frac{1}{6}\right)$ |
| Row 4 | $\frac{1}{3}$ | $\frac{1}{6}$ | $\frac{2}{3}$ | $\frac{1}{6}$ | $\left(1\frac{1}{3}\right)$ |

$\left(3\right)\left(2\frac{1}{3}\right)\left(3\frac{5}{6}\right)\left(2\frac{2}{3}\right)$

2. $11\frac{5}{6}$
3. $11\frac{5}{6}$
4. yes

# Globs of Goo

**Goals**
- Divide with whole numbers.
- Understand the division algorithm.
- Use logical reasoning to solve problems.

**Notes**
Prior to doing this problem set, review the division algorithm for finding the quotient of a four-digit number divided by a two-digit number.

**Solutions to all problems in this set appear on page 95.**

**Globs of Goo 1**

**Questions to Ask**
- What number is the hundreds digit of the quotient? (3) How do you know? (24 × 3 = 72)
- What numbers are covered by the goo below 72? (1, 1) How do you know? (83 − 72 = 11)
- How can you determine the digit covered by the goo below the 0? (Since 4 × 24 = 96, the digit is 6.)
- How can you figure out the remaining digits? (Since the remainder is 0, 24 must divide 14_ evenly. Because 24 × 6 = 144, the last digit of the dividend is 4; the last digit of 14_ is 4; and the ones digit of the quotient is 6.)

**Solutions**
1.
```
        346
   24)8304
     −72
      110
      −96
      144
     −144
        0
```

2. Possible answer: Since the remainder is 0, 24 must divide 14_ evenly. Because 24 × 6 = 144, the last digit of 14_ is 4. Then 4 must also be the ones digit in the dividend.

# Globs of Goo  1

Oops! Globs of goo are covering eight digits.
Figure out what they are.

1. Write the digits on the goo.

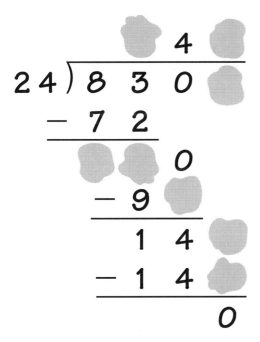

2. How did you figure out the ones digit of the dividend?

_____

_____

_____

# Globs of Goo ★ 2

Oops! Globs of goo are covering four digits.
Figure out what they are.

**1.** Write the digits on the goo.

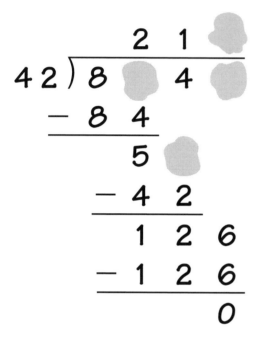

**2.** How did you figure out the hundreds digit of the dividend?

_____

_____

_____

# Globs of Goo  3

Oops! Globs of goo are covering five digits.
Figure out what they are.

1. Write the digits on the goo.

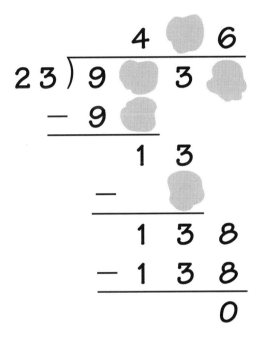

2. How did you figure out the tens digit of the quotient?

_____

_____

_____

# Globs of Goo  4

Oops! Globs of goo are covering five digits.
Figure out what they are.

**1.** Write the digits on the goo.

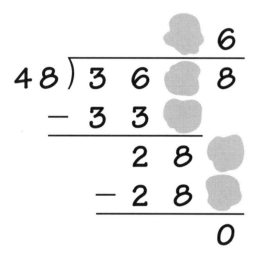

**2.** How did you figure out the ones digit of the first product?

_____

_____

_____

# Globs of Goo  5

Oops! Globs of goo are covering seven digits.
Figure out what they are.

**1.** Write the digits on the goo.

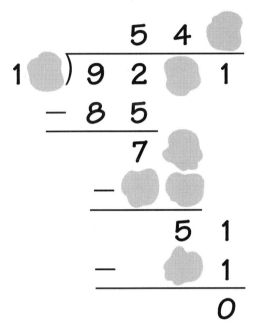

**2.** How did you figure out the tens digit of the dividend?

_____

_____

_____

# Globs of Goo ⭐ 6

Oops! Globs of goo are covering seven digits.
Figure out what they are.

**1.** Write the digits on the goo.

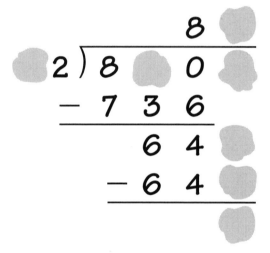

**2.** How did you figure out the ones digit of the quotient?

_____

_____

_____

# Solutions

## Globs of Goo  1

1.
```
        346
   24)8304
     −72
      110
      −96
       144
      −144
         0
```

2. Possible answer: Since the remainder is 0, 24 must divide 14_ evenly. Because 24 × 6 = 144, the last digit of 14_ is 4. Then 4 must also be the ones digit in the dividend.

## Globs of Goo  2

1.
```
        213
   42)8946
     −84
       54
      −42
       126
      −126
         0
```

2. Possible answer: Since 4 is being subtracted from this digit and the result is 5, the digit is 9.

## Globs of Goo  3

1.
```
        406
   23)9338
     −92
       13
       −0
       138
      −138
         0
```

2. Possible answer: 23 times the tens digit of the quotient gives a single-digit product. This number, when subtracted from 13, gives 13, so it is 0. Since 0 is also the product, the tens digit of the quotient is 0.

## Globs of Goo 4

1.
```
         76
   48)3648
     −336
       288
      −288
         0
```

2. Possible answer: The first product is 48 × _ = 33_. Since 48 × 7 = 336, the ones digit of the first product is 6.

## Globs of Goo  5

1.
```
        543
   17)9231
     −85
       73
      −68
        51
       −51
         0
```

2. Possible answer: First, find the ones digit of the divisor. Since 17 × 5 = 85, it is 7. Then the second product is 4 × 17 = 68. Write 6 and 8 on the goo below the 7 and the goo. Then think: What number minus 68 is 5? Since 73 − 68 = 5, write 3 next to the 7. Then 3 is also the tens digit of the dividend, since that was the number brought down to make 73.

## Globs of Goo  6

1.
```
         87
   92)8004
     −736
       644
      −644
         0
```

2. Possible answer: First, find the tens digit of the divisor. Since 8 × 92 = 736, it is 9. What number times 92 is about 640? Since 7 × 92 = 644, 7 is the ones digit of the quotient.

# Circle Sums

**Goals**
- Find sums of three addends.
- Identify sets of numbers with sums that match given sums.
- Recognize when certain sums share a common addend.
- Use logical reasoning to solve problems.

**Notes**
When checking solutions, note that students' solutions may be rotations or reflections of the given solutions.

**Solutions to all problems in this set appear on page 103.**

**Circle Sums 1**

**Questions to Ask**
- In Problem 1, how many circles are in each line? (3)
- How many lines of circles are there? (3)
- Will some numbers be in more than one line? (yes) Where are those numbers located? (in the corners)
- What is the sum of the numbers along each line? (38, 39, and 40)
- What is the sum of the numbers in all three lines? (117) What is the sum of the numbers 10 through 15? (75) Why are these sums different? (The numbers in the corners are counted in two different line sums.)
- What is the sum of the corner numbers? (42) How do you know? (The difference between 117 and 75 is the sum of the numbers that were counted twice.)
- What sets of three numbers from 10 to 15 have a sum of 42? (13, 14, 15)

**Solutions**
1. 42
2. 13, 14, 15
3. Possible answers:

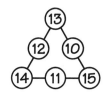 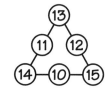

# Circle Sums  1

Use the numbers 10 through 15.
Record a different number in each circle.
The sums along the lines are 38, 39, and 40.

1. What is the sum of the three corner numbers? _____

2. What three numbers give this sum?

_____

3. Find two ways to solve the problem.

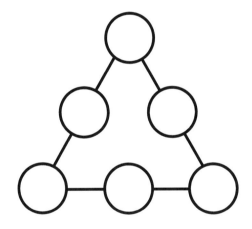 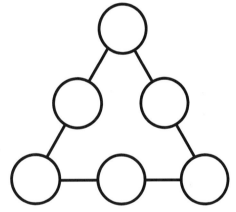

# Circle Sums ⭐ 2

Use the numbers 10 through 15.
Record a different number in each circle.
The sum along each line is 36.

**1.** What is the sum of the three corner numbers? _____

**2.** What three numbers give this sum?

_____

**3.** Find a way to solve the problem.

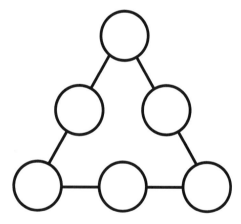

# Circle Sums ⭐ 3

Use the numbers 10 through 15.
Record a different number in each circle.
The sum along each line is 37.

1. What is the sum of the three corner numbers? _____

2. What three numbers give this sum?

_____

3. Find a way to solve the problem.

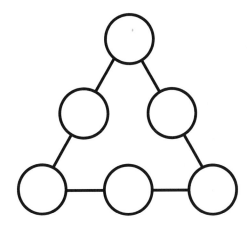

# Circle Sums  4

Use the numbers 10 through 15.
Record a different number in each circle.
The sums along the lines are 35, 36, and 37.

1.  What is the sum of the three corner numbers? _____

2.  What three numbers give this sum?

    _____

3.  Find two ways to solve the problem.

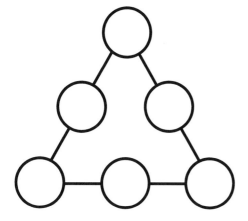 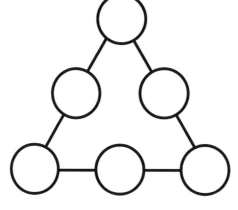

Name _____

# Circle Sums  5

Use the numbers 10 through 15.
Record a different number in each circle.
The sums along the lines are 34, 37, and 40.

1. What is the sum of the three corner numbers? _____

2. What three numbers give this sum?

   _____

3. Find two ways to solve the problem.

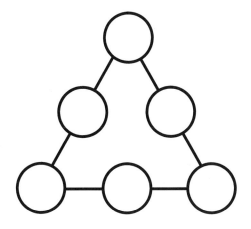
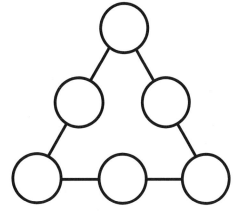

# Circle Sums  6

Use the numbers 10 through 15.
Record a different number in each circle.
The sums along the lines are 35, 38, and 41.

1. What is the sum of the three corner numbers? _____

2. What three numbers give this sum?

_____

3. Find two ways to solve the problem.

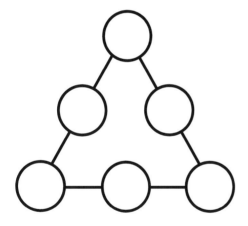 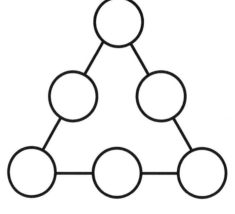

# Solutions

## Circle Sums ⭐ 1

1. 42
2. 13, 14, 15
3. Possible answers:

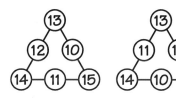

## Circle Sums ⭐ 2

1. 33
2. 10, 11, 12
3. Possible answer:

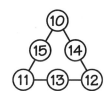

## Circle Sums ⭐ 3

1. 36
2. 10, 11, 15; 10, 12, 14; and 11, 12, 13
3. Possible answer:

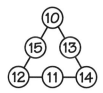

## Circle Sums ⭐ 4

1. 33
2. 10, 11, 12
3. Possible answers:

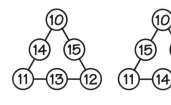

## Circle Sums ⭐ 5

1. 36
2. 10, 12, 14; 11, 12, 13; and 10, 11, 15
3. Possible answers:

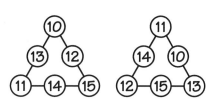

## Circle Sums ⭐ 6

1. 39
2. 12, 13, 14; 10, 14, 15; and 11, 13, 15
3. Possible answers:

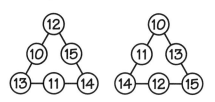

# Shape Numbers

**Goals**
- Identify numbers from clues provided in equations.
- Compute with whole numbers.
- Compute with exponents.
- Follow the rules for order of operations.

**Notes**
Point out to students that equations often cannot be solved in the order in which they are presented. After students have found the values for all shapes, have them check each equation to be sure that the left side equals the right side. Some students may be interested in developing their own shape-number equations to exchange with others.

**Solutions to all problems in this set appear on page 111.**

**Shape Numbers 1**

**Questions to Ask**
- What are the numbers on the sign? (0, 3, 4, 6, 7, 9)
- Which equation can you solve first? (Equation C) Why? (It has only one shape, the triangle.) What number belongs in the triangle? (4) How do you know? (The triangle squared means a triangle times a triangle, so the numbers are the same: $4 \times 4 = 16$.)
- What shape can you solve for next? (the circle in Equation E; the rectangle in Equation F) What is its value? (the circle is 3; the rectangle is 9)
- How did you find the value? (In Equation E, subtracting 4 from both sides yields 8 times the circle equal to 24, so the value of the circle is 3. In Equation F, 36 is equal to 4 times the rectangle, so the value of the rectangle is 9.)

**Solutions**
1. A. $9 \times 6 = 54$  D. $9 + 3 = 2 \times 6 + 0$
   B. $0 + 7 = 7$  E. $4 + 8 \times 3 = 4 \times 7$
   C. $4^2 = 16$  F. $(4 + 8) \times 3 = 4 \times 9$
2. Possible answer: From Equation C, the triangle is 4. From Equation E, the circle is 3. From Equation F, the rectangle is 9. From Equation A, the square is 6. From Equation D, the pentagon is 0. From Equation B, the hexagon is 7.

# Shape Numbers  1

Fill in the shapes with numbers from the sign.
Same shapes have same numbers.
Different shapes have different numbers.

6    4
7
9    3
0

1. Write the numbers in the shapes.

A. $\boxed{\phantom{xx}} \times \boxed{\phantom{x}} = 54$

B. ⬠ + ⬡ = 7

C. $\triangle^2 = 16$

D. $\boxed{\phantom{xx}} + \bigcirc = 2 \times \square + ⬠$

E. $\triangle + 8 \times \bigcirc = \triangle \times 7$

F. $(\triangle + 8) \times 3 = \triangle \times \boxed{\phantom{xx}}$

2. How did you figure out the number for the ⬡ ?

_____

_____

_____

# Shape Numbers ★ 2

5     6
  0
8     3
  2

Fill in the shapes with numbers from the sign.
Same shapes have same numbers.
Different shapes have different numbers.

1. Write the numbers in the shapes.

A. ☐ + 2 × △ = 11 + ☐

B. (☐ + 2) × △ = 25 + ⬡

C. ◯ − ⬠ = ☐

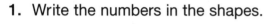
D. 9 = ☐²

E. ☐ + △ = ◯

F. △² = 25

2. How did you figure out the number for the ⬠ ?

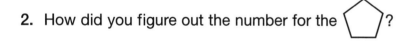

_____

_____

_____

# Shape Numbers ⭐ 3

Fill in the shapes with numbers from the sign.
Same shapes have same numbers.
Different shapes have different numbers.

Sign numbers: 1  4  0  3  9  7

1. Write the numbers in the shapes.

   A. ☐ = 12 − ⬠

   B. △ + ⬡ = ☐ − 2 × ▭

   C. ◯² − 14 = 35

   D. ◯ × 4 = (☐ − 2) × ▭

   E. ⬠² = 10 − △

   F. ☐ × ◯ − 6 = 57

2. How did you figure out the number for the ☐ ?

   _____

   _____

   _____

# Shape Numbers  4

Fill in the shapes with numbers from the sign.
Same shapes have same numbers.
Different shapes have different numbers.

20　　0
90
30　10
80

1. Write the numbers in the shapes.

A. ▢ × 3 = ⬡

B. ⬡ − ◯ = ⬠ + 10

C. △ = 40 − ▢

D. ( ⬡ + △ ) ÷ 5 = ▭

E. 65 = △² − 35

F. ⬡ + △ ÷ 5 = ◯ + △ + 2

2. How did you figure out the number for the ⬠ ?

_____

_____

_____

# Shape Numbers ★ 5

Fill in the shapes with numbers from the sign.
Same shapes have same numbers.
Different shapes have different numbers.

1. Write the numbers in the shapes.

   A. ☐ − ◯ × 2 = ⬠

   B. ◯$^2$ = 105 + 295

   C. △ + ⬡ − 3 = 97

   D. ☐ + ◯ ÷ 2 = ⬡

   E. (☐ + ◯) ÷ 2 = ☐

   F. ◯ × △ = 200

2. How did you figure out the number for the ☐ ?

   _____

   _____

   _____

# Shape Numbers  6

30        10
    40
70        90
    20

Fill in the shapes with numbers from the sign.
Same shapes have same numbers.
Different shapes have different numbers.

**1.** Write the numbers in the shapes.

A. $\bigcirc^2 - \triangle^2 \times 3 = \square + \triangle$

B. $(\bigcirc^2 - \triangle^2) \times 3 = 900$

C. $1{,}000 - \square^2 = 100$

D. $\pentagon \times \hexagon = 2^5 \times 5^2$

E. $100 - \bigcirc = \square$

F. $\triangle^2 + \square^2 = 1{,}000$

**2.** How did you figure out the number for the $\square$ ?

_____

_____

_____

# Solutions

## Shape Numbers 1

1. **A.** $9 \times 6 = 54$

   **B.** $0 + 7 = 7$

   **C.** $4^2 = 16$

   **D.** $9 + 3 = 2 \times 6 + 0$

   **E.** $4 + 8 \times 3 = 4 \times 7$

   **F.** $(4 + 8) \times 3 = 4 \times 9$

2. Possible answer: From Equation C, the triangle is 4. From Equation E, the circle is 3. From Equation F, the rectangle is 9. From Equation A, the square is 6. From Equation D, the pentagon is 0. From Equation B, the hexagon is 7.

## Shape Numbers 2

1. **A.** $3 + 2 \times 5 = 11 + 2$

   **B.** $(3 + 2) \times 5 = 25 + 0$

   **C.** $8 - 6 = 2$

   **D.** $9 = 3^2$

   **E.** $3 + 5 = 8$

   **F.** $5^2 = 25$

2. Possible answer: From Equation D, the square is 3. From Equation F, the triangle is 5. From Equation E, the circle is 8. From Equation A, the rectangle is 2. From Equation C, the pentagon is 6.

## Shape Numbers 3

1. **A.** $9 = 12 - 3$

   **B.** $1 + 0 = 9 - 2 \times 4$

   **C.** $7^2 - 14 = 35$

   **D.** $7 \times 4 = (9 - 2) \times 4$

   **E.** $3^2 = 10 - 1$

   **F.** $9 \times 7 - 6 = 57$

2. Possible answer: From Equation C, the circle is 7. From Equation F, the square is 9. From Equation D, the rectangle is 4.

## Shape Numbers 4

1. **A.** $30 \times 3 = 90$

   **B.** $90 - 80 = 0 + 10$

   **C.** $10 = 40 - 30$

   **D.** $(90 + 10) \div 5 = 20$

   **E.** $65 = 10^2 - 35$

   **F.** $90 + 10 \div 5 = 80 + 10 + 2$

2. Possible answer: From Equation E, the triangle is 10. From Equation C, the square is 30. From Equation A, the hexagon is 90. From Equation F, the circle is 80. From Equation B, the pentagon is 0.

## Shape Numbers 5

1. **A.** $80 - 20 \times 2 = 40$

   **B.** $20^2 = 105 + 295$

   **C.** $10 + 90 - 3 = 97$

   **D.** $80 + 20 \div 2 = 90$

   **E.** $(80 + 20) \div 2 = 50$

   **F.** $20 \times 10 = 200$

2. Possible answer: From Equation B, the circle is 20. From Equation F, the triangle is 10. From Equation C, the hexagon is 90. From Equation D, the rectangle is 80. From Equation E, the square is 50.

## Shape Numbers 6

1. **A.** $20^2 - 10^2 \times 3 = 90 + 10$

   **B.** $(20^2 - 10^2) \times 3 = 900$

   **C.** $1{,}000 - 30^2 = 100$

   **D.** $40 \times 20 = 2^5 \times 5^2$

   **E.** $100 - 70 = 30$

   **F.** $10^2 + 30^2 = 1{,}000$

2. Possible answer: From Equation C, the square is 30. From Equation F, the triangle is 10. From Equation B, the hexagon is 20. From Equation A, the rectangle is 90.

# Order, Please!

**Goals**
- Compute values of numerical expressions by applying the rules for the order of operations.
- Compute with whole numbers.
- Compute with exponents.
- Identify the factors of numbers.
- Use logical reasoning to solve problems.

**Notes**

Prior to doing this problem set, review the rules for the order of operations: evaluate expressions within parentheses, evaluate expressions with exponents, do multiplication and division from left to right, and then do addition and subtraction from left to right. There are multiple ways to complete many of the number sentences because multiplication and addition are commutative.

**Solutions to all problems in this set appear on page 119.**

### Order, Please! 1

**Questions to Ask**
- (Write the following expression on the board: $(4 + 3)^2 - (2 + 5)$.) What operation will you do first? (Add the numbers in parentheses: $4 + 3 = 7$ and $2 + 5 = 7$.) What will you do next? (Square the 7: $7 \times 7 = 49$.) What is the value of the expression? (42)
- Look at Problem 1. What is the sum? (26) Could the squared number be 5? (no) Why not? (Because $5^2$ is 25, and adding the other three numbers brings the sum to 34)
- Could the squared number in Problem 1 be 2? (no) Why not? (Because $2^2$ is 4, and adding the other three numbers brings the sum to 15)

**Solutions**
1. Possible answer: $4^2 + 5 + 3 + 2 = 26$
2. Possible answer: $(3 + 4) \times (5 \times 2)^2 = 700$
3. Possible answer: $4 \times 5 \times 3 \div 2^2 = 15$
4. Possible answer: $(4 + 3)^2 - (2 + 5) = 42$

# Order, Please!  1

Use every number on the sign once
in each sentence.
Use the rules for the order of operations
to make each sentence true.

1. _____$^2$ + _____ + _____ + _____ = 26

2. (_____ + _____) × (_____ × _____)$^2$ = 700

3. _____ × _____ × _____ ÷ _____$^2$ = 15

4. (_____ + _____)$^2$ − (_____ + _____) = 42

# Order, Please!

Use every number on the sign once
in each sentence.
Use the rules for the order of operations
to make each sentence true.

1. ( _____ − _____ )² + ( _____ − _____ )² = 8

2. _____ × ( _____ + _____ + _____ )² = 144

3. _____ + _____ + _____ − _____ = 4

4. _____² + _____ + _____ − _____ = 20

# Order, Please!  **3**

Use every number on the sign once
in each sentence.
Use the rules for the order of operations
to make each sentence true.

1. _____ × _____ − _____ × _____ = 9

2. (_____ + _____)$^2$ + _____ + _____ = 108

3. (_____ + _____)$^2$ − (_____ + _____)$^2$ = 0

4. _____ × _____ − _____$^2$ + _____ = 20

# Order, Please!  4

Use every number on the sign once
in each sentence.
Use the rules for the order of operations
to make each sentence true.

1. $(\underline{\quad} + \underline{\quad})^2 \times (\underline{\quad} + \underline{\quad})^2 = 10{,}000$

2. $(\underline{\quad} + \underline{\quad}) \div \underline{\quad} + \underline{\quad}^2 = 71$

3. $\underline{\quad} - \underline{\quad} + (\underline{\quad} + \underline{\quad})^2 = 38$

4. $\underline{\quad} + \underline{\quad} + \underline{\quad}^2 + \underline{\quad}^2 = 106$

# Order, Please!  5

Use every number on the sign once
in each sentence.
Use the rules for the order of operations
to make each sentence true.

1. (_____ − _____)² × _____ − _____ = 47

2. (_____ + _____² + _____) × _____ = 160

3. (_____ − _____)² − _____² − _____ = 22

4. _____ − (_____ − _____)² × _____ = 2

# Order, Please!  6

Use every number on the sign once
in each sentence.
Use the rules for the order of operations
to make each sentence true.

5  9
7  3

1. (_____ + _____ + _____) ÷ _____ = 7

2. _____$^2$ − _____$^2$ − _____ − _____ = 46

3. [(_____ + _____) ÷ _____]$^2$ × _____ = 12

4. (_____$^2$ − _____$^2$) ÷ (_____ + _____) = 4

# Solutions

### Order, Please!  1

1. Possible answer:
   $4^2 + 5 + 3 + 2 = 26$

2. Possible answer:
   $(3 + 4) \times (5 \times 2)^2 = 700$

3. Possible answer:
   $4 \times 5 \times 3 \div 2^2 = 15$

4. Possible answer:
   $(4 + 3)^2 - (2 + 5) = 42$

### Order, Please!  2

1. Possible answer:
   $(4 - 2)^2 + (3 - 1)^2 = 8$

2. Possible answer:
   $4 \times (3 + 2 + 1)^2 = 144$

3. Possible answer:
   $4 + 2 + 1 - 3 = 4$

4. Possible answer:
   $4^2 + 3 + 2 - 1 = 20$

### Order, Please!  3

1. Possible answer:
   $6 \times 4 - 3 \times 5 = 9$

2. Possible answer:
   $(4 + 6)^2 + 3 + 5 = 108$

3. Possible answer:
   $(6 + 3)^2 - (5 + 4)^2 = 0$

4. Possible answer:
   $6 \times 4 - 3^2 + 5 = 20$

### Order, Please!  4

1. Possible answer:
   $(8 + 2)^2 \times (6 + 4)^2 = 10,000$

2. Possible answer:
   $(6 + 8) \div 2 + 8^2 = 71$

3. Possible answer:
   $8 - 6 + (4 + 2)^2 = 38$

4. Possible answer:
   $2 + 4 + 6^2 + 8^2 = 106$

### Order, Please! 5

1. Possible answer:
   $(10 - 5)^2 \times 2 - 3 = 47$

2. Possible answer:
   $(5 + 3^2 + 2) \times 10 = 160$

3. Possible answer:
   $(10 - 3)^2 - 5^2 - 2 = 22$

4. Possible answer:
   $10 - (5 - 3)^2 \times 2 = 2$

### Order, Please!  6

1. Possible answer:
   $(9 + 5 + 7) \div 3 = 7$

2. Possible answer:
   $9^2 - 5^2 - 3 - 7 = 46$

3. Possible answer:
   $[(9 + 5) \div 7]^2 \times 3 = 12$

4. Possible answer:
   $(9^2 - 7^2) \div (5 + 3) = 4$

# Certificate of Excellence

## in Numbers

This is to certify that

_____

has satisfactorily completed all the problems for the big idea

_____

and is considered to be an expert.

Date _____    School _____

Grade _____    Teacher _____